THE AUTHORS

DARAN LITTLE left Manchester Polytechnic in 1988 with a BA (Hons) in film and television production. Since that time he has been employed at Granada Television as the archivist on 'Coronation Street' and 'Families'. In his three and a half years as archivist he has watched all 3,400 episodes of 'Coronation Street' and has written an in-depth synopsis of every storyline and character.

Daran is also the author of two other books on 'Coronation Street': 'The Life and Loves of Elsie Tanner' and 'The Ogdens of Number Thirteen'.

BILL HILL is the present editor of 'The Street' – the official 'Coronation Street' magazine. He has been associated with 'Coronation Street' and its merchandise since 1986. A true 'Street' fan, Bill has a collection of every episode from October 1981 onwards.

This book is dedicated to Tony Warren,
the genius who created *Coronation Street*

Other Coronation Street books from Boxtree:

Life in the Street Graeme Kaye
Coronation Street Quiz Book Graeme Kaye
Street Cred Anthony Hayward
The Life and Loves of Elsie Tanner Daran Little
The Ogdens of Number 13 Daran Little

WEATHERFIELD *Life*

DARAN LITTLE   BILL HILL

B[Ⅰ]XTREE

Published in association with

 G R A N A D A   T E L E V I S I O N

First published in hardback in 1992 by Boxtree Limited
First published in paperback in 1993

Text © Daran Little and Bill Hill
Coronation Street © Granada Television 1993
Photographs © Granada Television, except as stated in the acknowledgements.

10 9 8 7 6 5 4 3 2

A catalogue record for this book is available from the British Library

Editor : Mary Lambert
Design: Karizzma Enterprises Ltd
Jacket Design: Anita Ruddell
Picture Research: Daran Little
Typesetting: Sunsetters
Printed and bound in Italy by OFSA s.p.a.

BOXTREE LIMITED
Broadwall House
21 Broadwall
London SE1 9PL

ISBN 1 85283 444 5

CONTENTS

INTRODUCTION

In 1992 Coronation Street celebrates its 90th birthday. The street was originally built in 1902, although viewers only tuned into the residents and their lives in 1960. In this book we take you back into the history of Weatherfield and old favourites such as Ena Sharples, Annie Walker, Hilda Ogden and Elsie Tanner all tell their fascinating stories about their lives pre-1960.

Along with the rest of the country, Weatherfield experienced two world wars, the Depression of the 1930s and history-making events such as the abdication of King Edward VIII and the assassination of President John F. Kennedy. In the following chapters you will be able to discover what effect these events had on the inhabitants of a small Northern town, and, particularly, how an unknown back terrace grew into the bustling, modern street that it is today.

The early chapters of the book start with when the street was first built in 1902 and then you are taken through the years up to present-day life in 1992. Each chapter covers an era and the main story tells you what life was like for the people of *Coronation Street* at the time, while individual stories of characters are woven in. Some you will know well, such as Ivy Brennan, Des Barnes and Liz McDonald, but others from way back such as Dinky Low, Albert Tatlock's friend, publican's son Charlie Corbishley and post office worker Sid Hayes, you will never have met before.

If you're a true *Coronation Street* fan this book is a must for you to read from cover to cover, as you will discover facts about the street's colourful history, and its ever changing residents, that you will never have seen written before.

CHAPTER 1

PRE-1902: EARLY WEATHERFIELD

The Weatherfield Coat of Arms incorporates the industry of Weatherfield (The Bee), the main trade of Manchester (The Boat), and the Rose of Lancashire.

WEATHERFIELD LIES SOUTHWEST of Manchester in the North of England and has been a community since pre-Roman times. When the Romans arrived, it became the site of an important Roman fort and the area was called Paulium after Paulinus the fort commander.

In time it became the main Roman garrison in the Northwest and a civilian population flourished on supplying food and provisions to the fort.

When the troops moved out, the population dwindled and it became a quiet farming region known as Bellwether Field — the field of the belled ram. It was later abbreviated to Wetherfield, then in the last 300 years, to Weatherfield.

The growth of Manchester from a medieval village to a Georgian town and its subsequent trade owed a lot to the industry and transport development in Weatherfield, where the Main and Barton Collieries were opened in 1786 and the Bridgewater Canal in 1764. The canal's opening drew in industry to the surrounding area. Coal wharves, flour mills, dyers, cotton mills, log mills and salt and corn warehouses all sprang up in the vicinity of the canal. The former, flourishing Roman encampment was soon to be one of the nation's first industrial complexes.

From the 1780s onwards, housing began to spread out over the fields and farms which belonged mainly to the Swinton family, who had bought up most of the land from established landowners — the Blacks and Bridgewaters. New roads were built to link up with Manchester city centre and in the 1830s the Great Northern Railway viaduct was built to run through Weatherfield, carrying passenger and goods trains to Manchester's Liverpool Road station.

The population of Weatherfield had by this time increased to about 50,000 as the factory owners took advantage of the available land so near to the city centre. The meat distribution trade flourished in the south-east corner of Weatherfield after the building of the abattoir and establishment of a market dealing with the hide and fat by-products.

In 1891 Sir Humphrey Swinton closed down the Barton Colliery and built further homes and factories on the site. In 1900 the oldest dwellings in Weatherfield, on the old Roman road, were demolished to make way for Rosamund Street, the new main road to Manchester with shops, housing and an infirmary.

This new road was named Rosamund Street after Sir Humphrey

Swinton's mistress, Rosa Hanbury, who, as a serio-comedienne, had been the toast of the London music halls in the 1890s.

≈ ROSA HANBURY ALIAS ≈ MABEL GRIMSHAW

Rosa Hanbury's most famous song, with words and music written by Bobby Tinker from the music shop. The sheet music sold in thousands at four shillings (enough to keep a Weatherfield family of four in food and lodgings for a week). Rosa received one penny for every copy sold.

'All my life I've searched for one thing. That is why I went on stage. I wanted to belong. Well, I think now I have found that I do belong.'

It is almost certain that the name of Rosa Hanbury would mean nothing in Weatherfield as it is today, even though Rosamund Street is named after her — it is *absolutely* certain that if someone mentioned her real name, Mabel Grimshaw, it would draw a complete blank.

But way back in the Naughty 1890s when the music hall was in its prime, Rosa Hanbury was a household name and the piano seats of Weatherfield would have contained, as all over the country, a copy of the music for Rosa's most acclaimed and most requested song *'If only you could love a girl like me (I would only love a boy like you)'*.

In 1895 Rosa and her song were the toast of the music halls — she had appeared at Daly's, The Oxford and The Alhambra and was rumoured to have entertained royalty on more than one occasion.

She had been brought up in a slum dwelling in which she and her five brothers and sisters shared two small rooms with their drunken father, Archie Grimshaw, and their hard-working, but weak-willed mother, Agnes.

The head of the household was a disgrace to mankind — lazy, foul-mouthed and a drunk. His wife, a wizened skeleton of 30, but who looked 50, did all she could for the children with the little she made from sewing on buttons, but there was little left after Archie had plundered her purse for drinking money.

To get away from home, Mabel managed to slip away to Sunday School where she was a model pupil and quickly learned to read and write, a talent that escaped her parents for their entire lives.

Her brothers and sisters, like their father, had little desire to learn and even when very young they modelled themselves on the lifestyle of the despicable Archie. Mabel was therefore quite delighted when Agnes told her a secret she had kept for the past eleven years — she was not a Grimshaw. She had been left in the care of newlyweds, Archie and Agnes, by a young chambermaid called Beatrice who had been in service with Agnes in a big house in Hackney. Beatrice had been only too pleased to avoid the shame of producing a child out of wedlock, by passing her on to the apparently stable, newly-married couple.

Little did poor Beatrice realize into what a terrible situation she was placing her love child. She had received twenty pounds from the father, the wayward, musically talented son of the household (he later became a concert pianist), and passed this on to Agnes to cover little Mabel's early years. Mabel was to see none of this money as Archie Grimshaw rapidly spent it on drink down at the Twelve Bells.

Mabel felt released by the knowledge of her parenthood and at twelve years old moved to the Bluebell Tavern in Poplar, where Agnes had a sister who had married a sailor later stationed at Portsmouth. The sister recommended her 'niece' for a job in the tavern before leaving to join her husband.

Here, Mabel collected glasses, washed up and polished the floor. Often, as she hurried between the tables in the Hall of Harmony at the rear of the tavern, she would join in the choruses of the songs performed on the stage above, and her fine soprano did not pass unnoticed.

Before long, she was invited by the landlord Charlie Deakin up onto the stage where she made her debut as a singer singing *'The boy I love is up in the gallery '* to an enthralled audience, who joined in with each chorus and responded to every gesture of the little songstress.

Charlie was delighted with his discovery and magnanimously paid her five shillings a week, allowing her time to practise and to visit a music shop in Bishopsgate where she could obtain the latest sheet music. Young Bobby Tinker, who always served her, was really taken by Mabel and was impressed with her musical ability. Often the little shop resounded as Bobby played the latest piece from the Halls and even operetta on the piano and Mabel joined in.

It was after one of these unrehearsed performances that a foreign looking man, elegantly dressed in a silk hat and cape, overheard the performance, and came in from the street and handed her his card. He introduced himself as Louis Rambaud, the owner and manager of the Coronet Theatre in Hackney, and said he would like to book Mabel to appear on his bill for the next Saturday night.

Charlie, although deprived of Mabel for his own Saturday night performance, readily agreed and gave her the rest of the week to practise for the big night. She appeared for the first and only time under her real name; her future performances were under the billing of Rosa Hanbury which M. Rambaud assured her was a name more befitting her delightful singing.

Never one to forget old friends, Rosa continued to buy her music from Bobby Tinker, who presented her with a hand-drafted copy of his own composition, *'If only you could love a girl like me'*, which he dedicated to her. This became the most requested song in her repertoire. Bobby continued to compose and later was to make his living from songwriting.

It wasn't long before Rosa was getting bookings in the West End and one night she met an admirer who was to change her life. The magnificent bunch of roses and dignified calling card, stating that Sir Humphrey Swinton begged to see her, was no more than she was used to, but somehow she felt obliged to respond and sent word to have him sent up. As soon as she set eyes on the distinguished gentleman who entered her dressing room she was entranced.

Sir Humphrey was from the North of England and owned a huge area of land south of Manchester. As their relationship flourished, he was able

Sir Humphrey Swinton photographed at Cambridge in 1885. Having been educated at Sedburgh, he studied architecture and went on to design several notable buildings in Weatherfield, including the Infirmary.

to tell Rosa of the sad circumstances in which he now found himself. He was the head of the Swinton family and controlled its wealth. At home in Weatherfield he had an elderly mother and a wife, Helen, who suffered from mental illness. She had become ill soon after their marriage and had gone from a fun-loving, much-admired local beauty to a moody, violent person.

With his wife's every need catered for by a private nurse and her own doctor, Humphrey had felt justified in taking leave of absence occasionally to spend short spells in London where he could indulge his passion for the theatre and enjoy the company of his sociable friends away from the constrictions of Weatherfield.

Rosa was the first and only lover he had taken outside his marriage and she was able to provide him with all the happiness and joy now missing from his marriage.

Helen's days were numbered and, although he did not confess it to Rosa, so were his. Like his father and his grandfather before him, he suffered from an incurable heart condition, which worsened when they were in the prime of life and apparent peak of health.

Watney Street Sunday market where Archie Grimshaw's children begged and stole. In the middle of the market was the Ebenezer Mission, a haven for Mabel Grimshaw where she learned to read and write.

What little time Humphrey had left he wanted to spend with his new-found love Rosa. So when Helen Swinton finally breathed her last, Rosa looked forward to becoming the second Lady Swinton. Unfortunately this union had to be delayed as Humphrey, worried about his mother's health, decided not to upset her by marrying someone she would consider to be just a chorus girl.

He begged Rosa to wait, and she agreed to go north with him where

Rosa Hanbury in her prime. The picture is taken from a postcard which sold very well for many years after her retirement.

he set her up in a fine house in the Oakhill area of Weatherfield not far from his own residence in Swinton Grange.

With time running out, Sir Humphrey was keen to complete his plan for a new Weatherfield — a haven for the workers from the mills and coal mines on his land. His plan included new shops, dwellings, schools, an infirmary, larger warehouses and places of entertainment to be built right along the main thoroughfare, and a public house on Commercial Lane.

Rosa joined him in his enthusiasm for this new Utopia and took great pleasure in assisting him in its planning. She was delighted when he renamed Commercial Lane 'Rosamund Street', after her. Then he started the building works.

Two of the new streets, placed back to back, were to be Mawdsley Street, completed and opened in 1900, and Albert Street, named after the Queen's late consort. But the death of Queen Victoria in January 1901 meant everybody was anticipating a coronation and Albert Street was renamed Coronation Street in the spring of 1902.

Sadly, Sir Humphrey died only weeks before Coronation Street was officially opened and occupied. In spite of the great shock of Sir Humphrey's death, Mabel soldiered on and saw the job completed, during which time she won the respect and admiration of her peers and the heart of the residents of the new dwellings.

The final transaction of Sir Humphrey's dream was the opening of the Rover's Return. It was Rosa Hanbury who attended the opening ceremony, but it was Mabel Grimshaw who stepped down from the platform.

She was now a leading citizen of Weatherfield and never again was she to tread the boards nor use the name, which had brought her so much fame.

✑ THE OPENING OF THE ROVER'S RETURN ✑

Saturday 16 August 1902 was a day that promised much. The sun shone brightly and the new brickwork of Coronation Street looked pristine in the presence of all the finery assembled on the platform erected at the end of the street, adjacent to the newly painted public house on the corner.

The crowd of people who assembled around it in their Sunday best knew what lay beneath the large Union Flag that covered its sign. They had seen Charlie Mason the signwriter at work for the last two weeks and observed his laborious execution of the title which he had completed in rich gold, yellow and green.

Coronation Street was at last to have its own hostelry. After a year of travelling to the Flying Horse in Jubilee Terrace for ale or, for the more adventurous, the Prince Albert in Inkerman Street, the hard-earned cash of its residents would soon be destined for a place nearer home.

From the platform, where an affluent batch of citizens gathered, came the sound of clapping as the frock-coated Charles Hardcastle, local mill owner and employer, called for silence during the speech of the raffish

Charles Hardcastle owned the cotton mill on Victoria Street and had a vested interest in the new houses in Coronation Street as they were built mainly to house his workers.

Aubrey Newton, the dashing bachelor who was the leading innovator of the brewery. He rowed for his college at Oxford and almost made the 1890 boat race crew.

Percy Oakes, the last line of the Oakes family. Ten years after his death the name Oakes was dropped by the brewery and it became Newton and Ridley.

Aubrey Newton who, beaming with good humour, stepped forward to begin his address.

'Ladies and Gentlemen,' he began in a voice already made throaty and deep by the fruits of his vocation, 'as chairman of Newton, Ridley and Oakes, I have come to add the finishing touch to the excellent work begun in June last year and completed by our guest of honour Miss Rosa Hanbury, whose great public spirit and consideration for the local residents has seen the ambitions of that noted benefactor, Sir Humphrey Swinton, fulfilled.

'It was he who instigated the building of these fine dwellings in Coronation Street and Mawdsley Street and also the places of work where most of you are able to earn your daily bread.

'His untimely death at a tragically early age may well have curtailed the progress of this excellent project had not his friend and confidante, Miss Rosa Hanbury, taken up the challenge and completed the job.' He inclined his head towards a small, pretty figure with blonde hair who blushed a little at this public acknowledgement.

A polite ripple of applause followed as Aubrey Newton continued: 'My fellow directors, Mr Leo Ridley' — he turned his head again towards a severe looking man of 60 or so in a charcoal grey suit and a bowler — 'Mr Percy Oakes' — a large man, loosely dressed and mopping his brow as he was acknowledged — 'and myself, are delighted to be called upon as representatives of the brewery, to perform a duty which I am sure will give great benefit to you all.'

His face assumed a solemn set. The guns of the Boer War, which have for so long threatened our peace of mind and plucked from our midst many of our favourite sons, have at last been silenced. Back from that bloody theatre has come one of our own, having achieved an heroic citation for his valiant deeds in the field of battle at Spion Kop in South Africa and later endured the hardships of capture and confinement by a barbarous hand.

'I refer to Lieutenant Philip Ridley who has now been repatriated from that savage land and has returned to join our family business.'

He flourished his hand towards a slim, fair haired young man who stepped modestly forward to be shaken by the hand by all the notables. He looked embarrassed as he received not only a handshake but a kiss from Miss Hanbury which elicited a round of polite applause from those nearby and the odd cheeky whistle from those leaning out of the upper windows along the street.

Silence was restored and Aubrey Newton, grasping the young hero's hand at his side continued: 'The name of our third and latest public house, which now sits shrouded before you, has been the subject of much discussion. His Majesty the King and Her late Majesty have been high on the list of the nominations for a title.

'However, great as the honour would be to assume a royal title, we have decided on a name closer to home. I have already introduced young Philip Ridley and now I have to say that his heroic effort in South Africa, so symbolic of so many gallant young men from this area, will not go uncommemorated.

'Accordingly, I call on Lieutenant Philip Ridley, our heroic rover who has finally returned, to reveal with pride the title of your new public house.'

Self-consciously the hero of Spion Kop stood forward, pulled the gold cord and revealed for the first time the green, gold and yellow sign — 'The Rover's Return' — so expertly applied by Charlie Mason.

The Rover's Return was ready to be occupied and Aubrey Newton handed over the keys to the landlord, Jim Corbishley, who unlocked the doors and threw them back with an extravagant gesture.

Coronation Street was now complete and was the definitive showpiece of Sir Humphrey Swinton's new Weatherfield.

In the Boer War, 1899-1901, Philip Ridley served with a Light Horse Brigade and won a citation for saving his Commanding Officer (and uncle), Colonel Ridley. He managed to disperse several Boers who had him trapped after his horse was shot from under him. Later Lieutenant Ridley was captured and saw out the remainder of the conflict in a prison camp.

CHAPTER 2

1902-1914:
WAITING FOR THE SUN TO SHINE

King Edward VII ascended the throne on 29 January 1901 at the death of his mother, Queen Victoria. Although well into middle age and having a reputation as a ne'er do well, he was still popular with the people and earned the title of 'The Peacemaker' by his efforts to make a peaceful Europe — he died in May 1910.

OLD QUEEN VICTORIA had been dead 17 months when the first residents were able to move into the newly built houses on Coronation Street. The street was originally to be named 'Albert Street' in memory of the Queen's beloved consort, as the street running parallel to the south, was named 'Victoria Street'. The completion date for the street was set at Friday 8 August 1902, which should have been two months after the coronation of King Edward VII. However, the future King's appendix had delayed the big event and the residents actually moved into the freshly painted houses on Saturday 9 August, the same day as the King was crowned. To mark the occasion landowner Mabel Grimshaw persuaded the Council to change the name of the street to 'Coronation Street'. The new name plates were hastily ordered and secured onto the buildings the following Monday.

The bosses at the local brewery, Newton and Ridley, Oakes and Company had been unhappy at the renaming of the street. Their staff had long prepared for the opening of the corner ale house on the street. The planned name for the public house was to be 'The Coronation'. It was felt that two Coronations was too much for one street, and as the street signs had already been erected, it was up to the brewery to come up with a new name, which it did — the Rover's Return, to commemorate the return of Lieutenant Philip Ridley from fighting in South Africa.

Once the disagreements over names had been sorted out, the new residents arrived at their new homes with their belongings piled on hand carts from the neighbouring streets. There was to be no grand opening, no speeches, no ceremony — all that had been planned for the opening of the public house. Instead, the new residents were handed keys to their dwellings by William Fazackery, who was the agent in charge of collecting the weekly rent of four shillings and six pence. For the majority of occupiers, this sum was to be the first of many changes in lifestyle; they were used to renting the old tenements in Baker Lane and Gas Street where the rent had never risen to above two shillings and six pence.

The rent, according to Fazackery, was fair and no one was going to argue with him. Each family felt privileged to have been allocated one of these new dwellings and they marvelled at all each one contained. Downstairs, the front door, with its top glass panel, opened onto a narrow hallway with stairs that lead up to the first floor. A new gas meter was fixed to the wall at the foot of the stairs. The first room you came across was the front parlour. From its window, you looked out on the rather dismal view of the rear of Hardcastle's cotton mill. Most of the residents also worked at the mill and had eagerly watched the building of the houses over the last few months from the tiny steamed-up mill windows.

The kitchen was the biggest room in each house. Along one side of it stood a huge black range, with an oven compartment and a chimney which climbed right up the stack. To either side of this dominating feature, wall units and drawers stood waiting to be filled. At the rear of the kitchen stood the scullery with its ceramic pot sink and door leading out into the back yard. The outside toilet was situated towards the gully wall, alongside the coal hole. Above the downstairs rooms, on the first floor, three bedrooms waited to be filled.

≫ THE HARRISONS' SECRET ≪

'What is wrong with keeping ourselves to ourselves? We do no harm.'

Enid and Lizzie Harrison had spent all their lives travelling from theatre to music hall, from circus to royal palace. They were gifted seamstresses but to their new neighbours they were a mystery.

The luxury of living in a new house in Coronation Street with three bedrooms was completely wasted on the two Harrison sisters when they moved in during August 1902. For all of their 67 years they had slept together, first as babies, on planks of wood bolstered by richly embroidered cushions; in later life on the cast iron bed in which their parents had died. To the new residents of Coronation Street, the Harrisons were 'the odd couple'. They were strangers to the area who kept themselves to themselves, and in company they had the annoying habit of speaking words that seemed to have no meaning. It was three months before Mr Thwaite, a local shop-keeper, concluded that they were speaking another language — French. French! Most of their neighbours had difficulty in even speaking the King's English, so used were they to their native dialect. And then there was the puzzling question the local women asked themselves: why did the rent man never call at the Harrisons' house? There was certainly something strange about the old ladies.

So, for the four months that Enid and Lizzie Harrison lived at Number 13 Coronation Street they made no friends in the street but just kept their own company. Except for Thursday afternoons, when the residents would watch as the two tiny figures, clad all in black, made their way silently down the street, past the Rover's Return Inn (which they had never entered) and turned right into Rosamund Street.

One afternoon, out of curiosity brought about by their mothers' continual gossiping, Vicky Makepiece and George Hewitt followed the two sisters. Their breathless report that the Harrisons had walked the length of Rosamund Street and finally crossed into the area known as 'Millionaire's Mile', caused even more gossip to be exchanged over the crowded back walls. If the true reason for those visits had also been known, the gossipers would have been quickly silenced.

Once they had left Rosamund Street the Harrisons would walk up to the new houses on Mount View and call on their old friend, Mabel Grimshaw, the one time music hall artiste, and now land owner. Settling themselves into her comfortable armchairs, they would allow themselves to relax and the sounds of their shrill laughter echoed as they reminisced about their travels abroad to places like France. Mabel would enthuse over the lavish costumes the ladies used to make for her, which enabled her to woo large audiences and even catch the eye of Edward VII. All three would then happily launch into a favourite song from those days on the boards. Lizzie's fingers, stiff from half a century of stitching, came alive as they pounded out the notes on a piano older than herself. Tea and muffins, dripping best butter onto the expensive Indian rugs, would be followed by Enid's favourite port and Lizzie's cigars. All too soon the time would come round to bid Mabel farewell and they would visibly shrink as they put on their tight black shawls and made their way back home.

Although the neighbours never discovered the real truth behind the Harrisons' outings, they did get a glimpse into their secret afternoons one cold November morning. A week earlier the newspapers had carried a report of a train crash in Stafford. Among the 24 people killed were two elderly ladies, dressed in black, one with the hint of port on her clothes, the other smelling of fine cigars. The ladies had died together, as they had been born together. No one ever found out why they had been on that train to Stafford, but on that cold winter morning a few days later, the local women gathered round at the church wall of St Mary's to watch the two coffins being lowered into the earth. The sole mourner was a finely dressed lady who threw rose petals into the grave before walking to the carriage that awaited her.

Percy Grimshaw, the first tenant of Number 1 Coronation Street.

The new occupants of Coronation Street, Mawdsley Street and Victoria Street were mainly mill workers, employed by Charles Hardcastle at his mill on Victoria Street or his warehouse on Rosamund Street. Hardcastle had built these towering buildings in the 1880s and their grand façades hid crowded weaving sheds, dye rooms and spinning houses. The work force had been recruited from the slums on the other side of the Railway Viaduct that cut through

Weatherfield. The buildings themselves were built on rented ground and the lease was now held by Miss Mabel Grimshaw. Charles Hardcastle was a man used to getting his own way, he was a hard employer who expected each of his workers to die, if necessary, for the firm. When some did die, mainly in the weaving shed as the women and children shot in and out underneath the looms trying to mend broken strands, he at least sent flowers to the funeral and paid for them to be buried in St Mary's graveyard without the indignity of a pauper's grave.

To coincide with the residents moving into Coronation Street, a non-conformist chapel was built opposite the corner shop so that the people had a place to worship and it was completed late in 1902.

≥ GLADYS ARKWRIGHT — THE SAVIOUR ≤ OF SOULS

'My armour's well girded. I'm ready for battle.'

The Christmas Eve 7 o'clock thanksgiving service was the first to be held at the new non-conformist chapel on Coronation Street in 1902. Situated next to the mill, by the railway arch and with its main entrance on Victoria Street, the Mission of Glad Tidings was to be the sixth chapel built in Weatherfield. The people in the street had worshipped at the Salvation Chapel on Clarence Street in the months leading up to Christmas. Now the new chapel was open, the irregular worshippers found themselves compelled to attend, in case they were accused of being 'heathen' by their pious neighbours. Dressed in their Sunday suits, redeemed from the pawn shop for the weekend, the residents crowded into the mission hall. At the door they were greeted by shopkeeper Cedric Thwaite, who was also a lay preacher. By his side stood Gladys Arkwright, the new mission caretaker.

Gladys was know by most of the congregation. She had attended the Salvation Chapel for many years and was a respected member of the community. Her husband had died after only one year of marriage and, now aged 40, Gladys had turned down many marriage proposals. She was a happy cheerful soul and was much liked by everybody. The only people who did not like her were the local publicans. Gladys was a familiar sight as she stood outside the local public houses each Sunday afternoon, lecturing on the evils of drink and upbraiding those people she knew had not attended chapel that day.

Gladys Arkwright had devoted her life to The Lord when she was six. Now, given the opportunity to run the Mission of Glad Tidings, she declared war on all the local publicans.

Jim Corbishley, the Rover's Return publican, had already clashed with Gladys when she had talked so convincingly about the plight of the habitual drinker that she had converted one of his best customers into a teetotaller.

Gladys was also well known to the local children because she was a member of the local Sunday School circuit and visited each chapel in turn to deliver a talk, normally based on Daniel and the lions, which was her own particular favourite. Gladys saw it as her mission in life to win over as many children as possible to God and his chapel. Unlike the strict conformity of the Parish Church of St Mary's, Gladys was insistent that the new Mission would be a relaxed place of worship where people would be encouraged to visit. Gladys believed that with strong determination on her part, even all the committed sinners of Coronation Street could be saved.

The Rover's Return public house was heartily welcomed by the people of Coronation Street as they needed a place where they could go to drink and relax after their long working day. Do-gooder, Gladys Arkwright managed to convert some of the hardened drinkers away from the evils of alcohol, but most ignored her impassioned speeches in their rush to go and order their first drink of the day from publican, Jim Corbishley.

≫ CHARLIE IS ME DARLIN' ≪

'I'm a born romancer me. Women are like fine port. The more I taste the more I want.'

Domino champion Charlie Corbishley was popular with men and women alike. The local womaniser charmed his way out of many fights.

Shawl or no shawl, heads always turned when Janey Atkinson strutted down the street. Men stared appreciatively at the young barmaid while women drew their shawls closer and spat contemptuously into the gutter.

Janey's decision to stop wearing the uniform knitted shawl of all Lancashire women had, just as she had anticipated, caused an uproar in Coronation Street. The sight of Janey walking out showing off her figure was too much to be tolerated by any self-respecting woman. The older matriarchs of the area, led by Pearl Crapper, complained to the Rover's Return's landlady, Nellie Corbishley, when they met on Plank Street market. Mrs Corbishley refused to take any responsibility for her new resident member of staff. She knew, as they all did, that Janey was little more than a back street slut and had herself asked her husband Jim to send the girl back to where she belonged. But Jim Corbishley had a soft spot for the girl; she served behind the bar well, was popular with the male customers and, lacking bar experience, was cheap to employ. 'So long as she does no one any harm,' he had told Nellie, 'she can stay.'

If Janey was going to stay then Nellie was determined to make life as hard as possible for the poor girl. But no amount of sweeping sawdust around the public bar floor or emptying the spittoons could dampen Janey's natural good humour. She even started to sing in the bar on Friday nights, with Charlie Corbishley accompanying her on the piano.

Charles Corbishley had been seventeen when his parents sold up their Salford grocers shop for £40 and moved to Weatherfield to become the first tenants of the Rover's Return Inn. He had been happy to swap his grocer's apron for the job of potman in the pub, helping his father to keep the cellar organized and to throw out drunks when time had been called. It was also Charlie's job to wait on people in the Select bar if anybody wanted to drink in there where beer was a farthing extra because of the waiter service. Jim thought the Select was a waste of space as no one ever drank in it, but Nellie always insisted on a fire being lit every night, just in case.

Charlie looked much older than his tender years and he adopted a mature outlook on life. He had discovered the pleasure of whisky at the age of fourteen and, a year later, in his father's stock room had found something to better it — women. Charlie was a natural charmer and smooth talker, and to his delight on moving to the new area he found many young girls locally who fell for his good looks and gentlemanly manners. Unlike their brothers, boyfriends or even husbands, Charlie was not always covered in soot and dried sweat from working 16 hours in hot, crowded mills. Charlie pampered these young women, he flattered them and drew them to him with his smooth charm.

Maggie Leeming, two years Charlie's senior, was happy to deceive her husband Jack to spend some time with him. In fact she hardly tried to hide her love for Charlie, even to the point of waving to him from the Snug room of the pub. Charlie grew concerned about her blatant actions as he did not want to be forced into a fight with mill sorter Jack who was a lightweight boxing champion. Taking his father's advice, Charlie quietly dropped Maggie and turned his attention to weaver Annie Rogers. Again she was a bad choice; Daniel Grimshaw from Number 1 Coronation Street had his heart set on marrying Annie and he wasn't going to let a tailor's dummy like Charlie Corbishley get his hands on her. Their public fight in Coronation Street provided entertainment for the neighbours and left Charlie with a black eye and the Rover's with a broken window after Daniel pushed his rival into it.

And then Jim employed Janey Atkinson. The year was 1903 and the neighbours were just beginning to get to know each other. The Piggott family had replaced the Harrison sisters at Number 13, the Leemings had left the street under darkness owing four months back rent and the Rover's had seen its first death. Ernie Popplewell had died in the Snug, aged 65, during a game of dominoes. He had been the street's oldest resident and had worked most of his life on the canals, first building them and then working them as a barge handler. Janey arrived at the pub on the day of his wake and was greeted by crowds of soberly dressed people using the occasion to get drunk. In the middle of the room, Ernie's son Harry —

Janey Atkinson was a native of Liverpool. She came to Weatherfield in 1903, pregnant and unmarried, and had to find a husband fast or face throwing herself on the mercy of the Council.

Clara Popplewell with son Herbert. All her married life she had suffered her father-in-law's criticism.

wearing his father's teeth — played the spoons, while his wife Clara lifted her black skirts to dance a jig. Janey's immediate reaction was to join in the fun, lifting her skirt to reveal a slim ankle and a bright red petticoat.

As soon as he saw the colourful petticoat Charlie knew this was the girl for him, a fun-loving girl with no inhibitions and who wouldn't cry 'ands off' if the right occasion arose. He did not have long to wait for such an occasion. Janey had answered Jim's advertisement for a barmaid and was hired on a three-week trial. She was given a room above the pub and one evening off a week. As well as her bar duties she was to help Nellie with the housework, sweep up and look after the horses of any travellers who wished to use the Inn's facilities. Janey recognized in Charlie a fellow free spirit and encouraged him when he let his hand wander down her blouse one night behind the bar. The next day they became lovers.

Janey gave her relationship with Charlie just two months before announcing her pregnancy on Christmas Eve 1903. She felt pleased with herself for succeeding in her plan to trap a man and pass off the baby she was now carrying as his. No one would question a premature birth under the circumstances of a quick wedding and she decided she'd done better for herself than anticipated; Charlie Corbishley really was quite a catch.

Charlie's emotions and feelings upon hearing he was to be a father were mixed; he hated the idea of being tied down in any way and believed himself too young to settle down with a wife and child. On the other hand Janey was so vulnerable and helpless that he felt a certain responsibility towards her, after all she did live under his father's roof.

When Nellie was told that her only son was prepared to marry the hired barmaid she was horrified. She had been suspicious of Janey's behaviour in the last few weeks — the way she appeared paler than before and took longer to perform her chores. Although the girl was only of slight frame she was obviously conscious of her growing stomach. It was also obvious to the older woman that Charlie could not be the baby's father; nature just did not work that quickly. No matter how she tried to hide the signs, Janey was more than two months pregnant.

That night Nellie Corbishley had a quiet word with the barmaid in the pub living room. No one ever knew what was said, but when the family awoke on Christmas morning Janey had gone. Janey was never seen again in Weatherfield. Charlie was told by his mother that the girl had decided to visit her mother 'to think things out'. For a week he missed her and worried about her, but then his head was turned by another young beauty and Janey was forgotten.

Higher up the social scale, industrialist Charles Hardcastle impressed Mabel Grimshaw with his generosity in contributing a large sum of money to the restoration of the local school house on Silk Street. Six months later, in July 1904, Mabel agreed to marry the

The pupils of the newly-opened Bessie Street School in 1904. Ena Schofield (front row, second from the right) presented Mrs Hardcastle, wife of the local mill owner, with flowers.

wealthy mill owner. The ceremony took place at St Mary's church and all the mill workers were given the day off in celebration. The school on Silk Street was renamed Bessie Street Factory School, in fond memory of Hardcastle's late mother Elizabeth. At the opening ceremony five-year-old Ena Schofield (later Sharples) presented the new Mrs Hardcastle with a pretty bunch of locally picked flowers. Ena, like the other pupils, was a mill worker's daughter and was to attend the school until she was ten. From the age of eight she was to be employed at Hardcastle's Mill as a part-timer, earning four pence a week. From the age of ten she would be employed full time.

Just as the families had settled in well in Coronation Street a tuberculosis epidemic hit Weatherfield in late 1904. Families crowded together in the terraced houses found they had no protection from the infectious illness once a family member caught it. The residents of Coronation Street were shocked to hear the news that the Hawkers at 3 Mawdsley Street had lost nine family members in a month. Once the illness took a hold of the community it lingered on for many years. It thrived in the dampness of the air.

The Hewitt family at Number 3 suffered the most in Coronation Street. Dolly Hewitt contracted TB whilst she was pregnant and the pain and discomfort she suffered added to the normal distress and danger of childbirth and both she and the baby died. Her children George and Betsy followed six months later whilst her husband Samuel caught the illness in 1906, but lingered on until 1909. Three months later, in January 1910, his second wife Gertie gave birth to twins: Molly and Dolly. Dolly only had a short life and succumbed to the illness aged three months.

Not everybody living in new houses and nearby streets worked in the mills. The local coal pit, which gave Weatherfield its industrial

Samuel Hewitt at Number 3 died of TB five years after his wife Dolly.

Gertie Pegg was the first Mrs Hewitt's sister. She married her widowed brother-in-law Sam in February 1905. Many commented that she'd been too quick to step into her sister's shoes.

history, was situated behind St Mary's church. The colliery mines ran directly underneath the new streets and some of the miners employed at the pit were housed in them, although most lived in the streets near the pit itself. The mills, factories and warehouses had all been built towards the end of the nineteenth century, but the coal works had been in operation for many years before that. A large proportion of the older inhabitants of old Weatherfield still worked at the colliery whilst their children and grandchildren preferred to spend their days working above ground.

The whole of Weatherfield was completely devastated in October 1906 when an underground explosion caused a mine to collapse, bringing down part of neighbouring Earnshaw's Mill and trapping 427 miners underground. Rescue workers trying to reach the trapped miners were hindered by the masses of hysterical women waiting for news of their husbands, fathers and sons. Only 34 men emerged alive from the caved-in pit head, the rest were declared dead after three days of intensive rescue operations. It was Weatherfield's greatest disaster, hardly a family was left untouched by grief. In Coronation Street, widowed Aggie Grimshaw mourned her dead son, Daniel, whilst Pearl Crapper buried two empty cardboard coffins in memory of her husband Albert and son Jack whose bodies were never recovered. The pit was closed down after the disaster and operations moved elsewhere.

≈ PEARL CRAPPER — ≈ SOON TO BE A WIDOW

The women of the Rover's Return Inn — barmaid Sarah Bridges, housekeeper Pearl and, seated, landlady Nellie Corbishley.

'What's the use of a set o' teeth when you've not seen meat this side of Christmas?'

The earth shook, windows cracked, plates smashed from dressers and the birds ominously stopped singing. The noise of the underground explosion seemed to ring in the air for hours although the accident itself was all over in two minutes. Nobody living in Weatherfield needed anyone to tell them the cause of the almighty roar in October 1906. As a body they rushed out of the factories, mills and houses and ran, carrying infants, tripping over cracked flagstones and uprooted cobbles, towards Weatherfield's Main Pit.

Pearl Crapper, in her role of housekeeper at the Rover's Return, had been swilling down the ale-stained flagstones in the pub's back yard. The earth's shudder caused her to fall and bang her leg against a barrel. Her employer Jim Corbishley was at her side in a moment and helped her to her feet whilst a cloud of dust blew towards them from the pit face. Without a word, Pearl lifted her skirts and ran out into the gully and onto Rosamund Street. She dodged a horse that was rearing out of control, and joined the women swarming together towards the pit. The sound of the clogs running on cobbles nearly matched the density of the explosion.

At the pit face nothing could be seen; a thick sooty cloud had formed and the onlookers coughed and spluttered as coal dust penetrated their eyes and filled their lungs. Pearl drew her shawl over her face in protection. Her mind raced as she tried to remember what shift her men were on. She couldn't remember the time and the sun was obliterated by the dust.

Feeling her way along the railings around St Mary's Church, Pearl pushed her way to the colliery buildings where she instinctively knew the air would be clearer. Horse-drawn engines carrying fire fighters thundered down Edward Street. Everywhere people milled around, nobody knew what to do; nobody knew what was going on. There was no sign of a fire but the air smelt of gas. A child separated from its mother screamed on the pavement and Pearl lifted it clear of all the rushing feet. People seemed to be entering the colliery buildings and someone was shouting excitedly to the crowds. Still holding the child, she pushed her way towards the brick buildings. A man had sheets of paper, full of miners' names currently on shift. She couldn't hear above the confusion.

Ronnie Crapper had been thrown to the ground by the explosion, at Bright's Pawn Shop where he was an apprentice. He had always suffered from a weak chest and his mother had kept him from joining his father and older brother down the pit. He helped the other men at the pit face as they tried to rescue the miners who had just been entering the mine face when the tunnel had caved in. He recognised his Dad's mate Charlie who was being helped over the rubble to be taken to the Infirmary. Ronnie rushed to Charlie asking him if he'd seen his Dad, or brother Jack but Charlie just stared blankly back through black and bloody eyes, his ears deafened by the blast.

Lanterns were lit as the day came to an end and the rescue operations continued throughout the night. The police persuaded most of the on-lookers to return home where they could then be easily contacted if there was any news about loved ones. Pearl refused to leave the pit face and together with Ronnie stood outside the Laughing Donkey pub waiting for news.

After three days the rescue operations were officially called off. A management spokesman informed the next of kin that all who could have been saved had been pulled from the rubble and that those men who were still missing would by now be dead. Only 34 miners had been rescued alive, 393 were still missing.

Ronnie Crapper (seated) had a weak chest, which prevented him from working down the pit and thereby saved his life. His brother Jack was killed alongside their father in a pit accident.

※

In the summer of 1910 the local brewery, Newton, Ridley, Oakes and Company, surprised and delighted the landladies in their twelve pubs by installing cast-iron bath tubs. Nellie Corbishley, like her fellow landladies, treated the tub with the awe it deserved. After forty years of bathing in front of the kitchen fire in a small tin bath, Nellie appreciated the luxury and privacy that accompanied the bath, set up in splendour in its upstairs room. Thanking the brewery

Unionist Fred Piggott preferred to spend his evenings drinking in the Rover's to being with his family, with whom he felt uncomfortable.

Ivy Makepiece's mother, Granny Harris, lay in state at Number 11 during a grave diggers strike. The stench from her decaying body upset the whole neighbourhood.

for their thoughtfulness, Nellie was shocked to discover the tub was intended to be a commercial venture; she was to encourage the local women to take advantage of the new bathing facility at a penny a time. She was horrified to learn, half of this money was to be included in the rent paid to the brewery!

With the closure of the coal pit, the men who had been employed there battled against school leavers for the few jobs that were on offer at the mills. The docks on the River Irwell to the south of town had their work cut in half as there was now no coal to be transported. The management had to cut wages to save money and laid off many men. The residents of Weatherfield found themselves forced to work for the few mill owners in operation, and had to accept low wages for the privilege. Unrest and discontent grew in the town as it did in other Northern towns in a similar situation.

Throughout the Northwest of England, workers closed down docks, factories and mills in a series of strikes. The people of Weatherfield joined their brothers and sisters, and marched on the Council offices to demand decent wages for hard work. Ships in dock on the River Irwell floated unmanned and their precious cargoes of food remained unloaded. Strike breakers were recruited from some of the pubs in the area. One such recruit was spotted in the Rover's Return by unionist Fred Piggott. He pounced on the man and the drinkers chased him from the street, throwing bricks at him as he ran. Fred was adamant that no one from his street was going to be a blackleg.

Later, Fred Piggott and his fellow unionists called on the mill workers, weavers and spinners to walk out at Hardcastle's. Charles Hardcastle tried to reason with his work force, when his pleadings failed he got angry and threatened to sack every man, woman and child. The workers refused to listen, they were fed up with trying to cope on a pittance, and were more than willing to listen to their union who were demanding a minimum wage of £1 for a 55 hour working week.

The deafening peace that hung over Weatherfield during that summer of 1911 was frightening to the people who could not remember a single hour of daylight which was not dominated by hooters, the clanging of machines and the clatter of clogs on cobbles as workers hurried to work.

As the days of strike stretched into weeks, the stench of the uncleared rubbish that lay in back alleys became unbearable. Starving cats and dogs roamed the area and died in the streets, where they lay for weeks. With no money to buy food, the people living in Coronation Street scavenged for scraps around the alleys, tried to catch fish with lengths of wire dangling in the canal and stole, in desperation, from the shops in an attempt to stay alive. The unions tried to help where they could, but the relief they had to offer was minimal. When Ivy Makepiece's mother died at Number 11 Coronation Street the family did not know where to place the body. The grave diggers were on strike and the undertaker's was full. Ivy tried to keep her mother as presentable as possible but as the body decayed the house smelt so badly when the door was open, that people stepped off the pavement as they went past to escape it.

Just as local shop keeper Mr Thwaite thought he would be bankrupted by his customers who were on credit, the Government agreed to some of the Unions' demands and the strikers returned to work. There had been angry scenes locally when mounted police had been called in to control rioting crowds. The chaos that had followed left cotton winder Clara Popplewell blinded in one eye after a policeman had lashed out at her with his truncheon.

The people of Weatherfield celebrated a return to work and more factories opened up to provide jobs for the unemployed miners and dockers. Ironically these workers would soon be taken out of the security of the factories to fight for King and Country.

◁ LOTTIE THWAITE — ▷ ALWAYS AN OUTSIDER

'I hear people say: "You have to be born around here to be able to cope with it." I think what they say is true.'

Lottie Thwaite from Germany knew very little English when she arrived in Weatherfield. To the people of Coronation Street she would always be an outsider.

Rosamund Street was crowded. It was market day and the air was filled with the sounds of traders, carts and gossiping women. Vegetable hawkers, rag-and-bone men, organ grinders and tub menders competed with beggars who sang for money and for road and air space. Lottie Hofner, travelling on a wagon containing all her worldly goods, sat bolt upright and held onto her hat while her new husband Cedric Thwaite tried to dodge the urchins who ran around his wheels, trying to peer under the fancy cloth which covered the wagon.

Lottie had arrived in England only two months previously and, with her faltering English, found the sight of busy Rosamund Street terrifying. She noted with some alarm that a herd of sheep were heading towards the wagon and shut her eyes in disbelief; this was a street, not a field. Sheep belonged in the country, not in towns. When she opened her eyes she found the wagon had come to a halt, the reason being that they were now surrounded by the bleating animals. Cedric smiled reassuringly at her and patted her arm. She tried to smile back but it was a very weak attempt.

As they turned into Coronation Street, the bustle continued. Women knelt cleaning their doorsteps. Children ran around playing in the street, some had no trousers on. They all laughed and seemed to be playing a funny game with a length of twine. A group of men stood outside the public house, they stared as she passed. One of them spat a lump of tobacco into the gutter, much to her disgust. The wagon stopped at the end of the street and Lottie saw for the first time the shop that was to become her home. She noted with approval its clean and fresh paintwork and that the window display was neat and tidy.

Cedric helped her down from the wagon and led her into the shop. She was aware of faces peering from houses. As they entered the living quarters behind the shop, Lottie thought she could hear a sheep bleating. Cedric heard the noise too and went to investigate. He found the Piggott twins in his back yard trying to silence a frightened ewe. Telling them to shut the animal up, Cedric gestured for the lads to take the animal next door to their own home where he could hear their father sharpening his knife in the yard. Lottie could not believe her misfortune; not only was she miles away from her parents in Germany, married to a man she hardly knew, but she was to live amongst people who stole sheep on their way to market and actually intended to eat the animal.

Lottie's family had sent her to England to broaden her mind. She had arrived with a cousin whose mother had married and settled in Fleetwood. The following weekend she had been taken to chapel where the guest speaker was Cedric. As a respected lay preacher he often found himself called upon to speak in other towns but this was the first time he'd travelled as far as Blackpool. Lottie had no idea what he had spoken on as she could not easily understand the language, but he had a lovely smile and his eyes twinkled. After the service they had broken down their language barrier by discovering they both spoke French and read music.

Lottie had no intention of finding a husband in England, but then she mused to herself, God works in mysterious ways. They had been married in Blackpool in the summer of 1912 and now she was to help him in his shop and in her spare time play the organ at the Mission across the road. Cedric had promised to give her English lessons each evening and she found his courteous manner very encouraging. She was certain she would soon be able to communicate with the customers.

The news that the new Mrs Thwaite was German spread around the locality in less than a day. Mothers and their children came into the shop purely to stare at this new foreign person, and Cedric cheerfully remarked that Lottie was good for trade. Gladys Arkwright from the Mission was very considerate and took Lottie under her wing, advising her what to wear so as not to offend the local women. Lottie put all her fine clothes away in drawers and reluctantly donned the shopkeeper's apron. She did, however, draw the line at wearing clogs, and instead she wore her black court shoes.

Lottie soon discovered the sheep incident was commonplace in Weatherfield, with two or three families working together a sheep could easily be manoeuvred down the back gully whilst the herders were busy with the main flock. The animal would then be hidden and kept quiet until the flock had passed. For the next week each family in Coronation Street ate like kings. When mutton wasn't on the menu, most families relied on credit from the Thwaites to see them through until pay day on Friday. Lottie soon learnt which families were to be trusted beyond the standard tick limit, and when to deny credit, despite threats and shouting.

For the three and a half years Lottie lived in Weatherfield she was never totally able to break down the neighbours' suspicions. She grew accustomed to conversations stopping as she passed women in the street, and grew to expect nothing more than a curt 'hello' from anyone other than Mrs Arkwright. Nevertheless, Lottie was happy with Cedric and the excitement he shared with her for the Lord really inspired her and made everything they did so worthwhile.

That was until October 1914. Britain had declared war on Germany two months previously and Lottie had felt very uncomfortable and confused as her loyalties became divided. Could she possibly return home to her parents in Germany or should she stay beside her husband? Should she mourn the loss of German or British troops, or both? She was now a naturalised British subject, had little accent left, and on the whole she considered herself English. The decision whether or not to leave England was made for Lottie on the night of 25 October. It was a Sunday night and she had played the organ as usual at the Mission. Everything seemed the same as normal until nine o'clock that night.

The shop window made an incredible booming noise as it shattered backwards into the shop. Cedric had been reading aloud to Lottie in the back room at the time and, fearing burglars, rushed into the shop. He found the neighbours smashing their way through the glass. Panic rose in him as they turned on him, waving sticks and clutching bricks. They called him a 'Hun Lover' and pulled him into the street. Outside a mob had gathered. He recognized Fred Piggott from Number 13, the Bucks from Number 9 and Alfie Marsh. They were all his friends, his customers, his loyal congregation ...

Whilst Cedric struggled against the mob, Gladys Arkwright tried to reason with the people. Children started to throw stones at Cedric and blood gushed from a wound on his head. Lottie was forced onto the street where women set upon her, pulling her hair, smashing her glasses and kicking her as she lay on the floor. Suddenly the police arrived and the mob scattered. Only Gladys and the Thwaites remained in the street. The shop lay open, goods lay on the floor and around the street where the locals had taken advantage of the row to steal what they could.

Lottie was classed as an alien. Bloody and bewildered, she allowed herself to be locked in the cell at Tile Street police station. Cedric was with her, equally confused. They had done nothing wrong, they had committed no crime, yet they were to be caged like animals. They were victims, but of what? A world war or their bigoted neighbours?

Cedric Thwaite had started his business in 1902, when he bought Number 15 Coronation Street for £35. The brewery was vexed as it had planned to open a beer shop on the premises.

CHAPTER 3

1914-1918: IN THE SHADOW OF WAR

DON'T WASTE BREAD!

SAVE TWO SLICES EVERY DAY and Defeat the 'U' Boat

The poster was a major form of propaganda for the working classes during the war and acted as stimulants to 'Save Bread!' or 'Enlist Now'. One poster, very much to the point, said 'The Women of Britain Say Go!'

WEATHERFIELD WELCOMED THE declaration of war on 4 August 1914 with a patriotic euphoria, which had flourished after the Boer War.

Not a man doubted that the wretched Huns, who were savaging central Europe with a cruelty and an inhumanity previously unknown to man, would capitulate the moment they came face to face with the indomitable British soldiers.

While the regiments of Accrington, Oldham and Rochdale prepared for war with broomsticks as rifles, and schoolmasters and Town Hall clerks assumed the roles of officers, in Weatherfield, the Weatherfield lads gathered at the Red Rec for training under the supervision of Matthew Hardcastle, Charles Hardcastle's son who was an accountant at his father's mill.

Albert Tatlock, Dinky Low, Clarrie Ross and many young residents of Weatherfield willingly submitted themselves to drilling, hand-to-hand combat and exercises in the field. They later had lectures in military tactics at the Mission of Glad Tidings from their honorary CO, who, it was rumoured, had formally commanded a regiment in South Africa. The aspiring young soldiers of Weatherfield hung on his every word and reacted to his every utterance of British invincibility with a gleaming eye and occasional bursts of loud applause.

Like young men all over Britain, the Weatherfield Pals were primed for action and waiting anxiously for their call to serve their country.

≈ ALBERT GOES TO WAR ≈

'If you've been in a trench with a chap you know him. And he knows you. If you can still be pals after that you will always be pals.'

The summer of 1914 always brought back fond memories for Albert Tatlock. He was 19 and in full employment at Hardcastle's mill and his naturally thrifty nature ensured he and his young brother Alfred lived adequately, if not luxuriously, at their lodgings in Rosamund Street.

Since 1906, when their father followed their mother to any early grave, he had become head of the household and, with the kindness of Mary Osbourne, their aunt from Number 1 Coronation Street, who had always

When his parents died, Albert Tatlock was just old enough to keep lodgings in Rosamund Street and look after his young brother. Nine years later, in the trenches, the memories of happy days in Weatherfield kept him sane.

Clarence Ross had been brought up at the Flying Horse public house. It had been built in 1850 and named the Flying Dutchman after the racehorse that won the 1849 Derby. In 1905 the brewery renamed the pub for patriotic reasons.

Mary Tatlock had married Jewish tailor Thomas Osbourne despite his family's attempts to stop the ceremony. Thomas was shunned by his Jewish friends.

provided a cooked meal on a Sunday, they survived.

Albert was secretary of the Weatherfield Wheelers cycling club and he and his two best pals, Dinky Low and Clarrie Ross, would often set off early on Sunday mornings to cycle to the countryside. Their leisurely pace was never taxing, and conversation and high-spirited romps in the fields and country lanes often meant they never reached their destination.

How they all enjoyed those days in the prime of their youth, with some money in their pockets and a lifetime of Sundays to look forward to. But war was in the air, the Balkans seethed with unrest and instability and the European politicians constantly debated what the future held.

Often, the friends' roadside chats throughout that summer turned to these portentous events and their own possible involvement. They made a pact that, come what may, they would always stick together and look to each other for comradely support.

The announcement of the deadlines of 4 August 1914 sent a shudder through those who knew war, but to Albert, Dinky and Clarrie it was just another challenge and they were first in the queue to take the King's Shilling.

When they returned home after signing-up for the Lancashire Fusiliers and with instructions to report to the Fusiliers' Barracks, Bury, they strutted like peacocks in the face of the public acclaim. Jim Corbishley, caught up in the flood of burgeoning patriotism, invited them all into the Rover's and offered them free drinks all night. Not a great risk to his profits, as none of them drank alcohol, but they took up the offer and had a jolly night on lemonade.

A week later, Albert greased-up his Rudge-Whitworth for the duration, moved their few belongings into Number 1 Coronation Street with the Osbournes, saw Alfred settled there and, with a promise to be back before Christmas with a German helmet, joined Dinky and Clarrie in the tram queue to make their way to Bury.

The stern discipline of their training, and their Sergeant Major's constant reminders that they were only fit for using up the Kaiser's bullets, did little to dampen their spirits. When they returned to Weatherfield on embarkation leave, proudly displaying their new uniforms, they were received as heroes who had already won the war. Young Alfred was delighted to have a soldier-boy for a brother and followed Albert wherever he went, vicariously enjoying the glow of Albert's acclaim.

Their company left in late 1915 for France and the three pals were quickly thrust into the régime of the trenches. In spite of their expectations, there were no heroic charges across enemy ground, no man-to-man bayonet battles and no celebrations of victory over a defeated foe — just the day-to-day existence in muddy, stinking dugouts with the ominous rumblings of shellfire in the distance and the occasional sight of a biplane overhead.

Then came 1 July 1916 when the massive allied bombardment suddenly stopped and at 7.30am the Lancashire Fusiliers went over the top at the Somme. The High Command had told them they'd stroll over the enemy lines with their rifles on their shoulders. Nothing, they said, could survive their shelling.

They were so wrong — the deadly machine guns soon put them right, as the carefully placed barbed wire helped to sight the advancing infantrymen in the German gunners' aim. Even in the panic of self-survival, the three Weatherfield pals kept together until, dashing for the cover of a shell hole, Clarrie suddenly stopped dead in his tracks and crashed to the ground.

Albert dropped beside him and Dinky, who was slightly ahead, disappeared into the dust. One look told Albert that Clarrie was dying, and in that terrible moment Albert realized that even the Weatherfield Wheelers were mortal.

Dinky had disappeared and Albert was suddenly aware that he had been wounded in the thigh. With one last look ahead for Dinky he rolled down to the bottom of a shell hole where he found himself in the company of a badly wounded French Canadian soldier, who could speak no English.

By now, Albert knew the look of death and did what he could to ease the last hours of his stricken companion. They lay together for the rest of the morning during which time, by necessity, Albert learnt a few words of French and the Canadian received his first and only English lesson.

Pinned down and unable to move forward or backwards, Albert took stock of his own wound, which was painful but not serious, and decided to wait for nightfall to make his way back to the lines. Whatever happened, he knew he was certainly out of the battle.

On his stumbling journey back from crater to crater he came across a crumpled figure calling for help who turned out to be Sergeant Boxer who had been with him since the training days in Bury. His leg was useless, as it was broken and shot through, and it was ironic that the powerful disciplinarian who had once filled Albert's days with terror was now vulnerable and helpless and looking to one of his 'useless specimens' for survival. Somehow Albert got himself and Boxer back to the stretcher bearers and they were carried away for medical attention.

After a spell in hospital, and then some time at a rehabilitation centre to recover, Albert was ready for action again, but not before a week's leave and a return to Coronation Street with a Lance Corporal's stripe on his arm.

A Weatherfield rover had returned to the street and Albert was cheered and praised wherever he went. To his delight, he learned that Dinky Low had made it back from that dreadful battlefield and was coming home to be married. It was a joyous week for Albert. First he found Dinky alive and well and then he was proud to stand as best man for him.

Before returning to the front, Albert and Dinky visited Clarrie's grief-stricken mother, who ran the Flying Horse pub in Jubilee Terrace. They were able to add facts to the basic details the 'missing in action' telegram had told them. She asked to be told of Clarrie's final moments and Albert was able to tell her that their son had died in the height of battle and had not had time to suffer.

Dinky and Albert returned to the front together where Albert survived

Albert sent this typically patriotic postcard soon after his arrival to fight in France in 1915. Even then, the censor would allow nothing that gave away his company's position or conditions.

Wilson's was the local cycling specialist, which stocked a fine selection of cycles as well as screws, nails and hinges. Percy Wilson, its proprietor, still owned a penny-farthing and his son, Digby, was a keen member of the Weatherfield Wheelers. Albert Tatlock bought his first Rudge from Wilson's in 1912.

the remainder of the war unscathed, in spite of winning the Military Medal for his action in rescuing two young infantrymen trapped by machine gun fire at Flers Courcelette.

When he returned home in early 1919, Albert was a changed man. Dinky's departure for London and Clarrie's death on the battlefield had left him virtually friendless — his youthful pursuits of 1914 were now just memories.

His brother Alfred, now 17, had left the area with the Osbournes, leaving only an address in Liverpool and a note to Albert saying he'd taken his bike as he needed it to get to work.

As Albert gradually got back into the routine at Hardcastle's Mill, his mind turned to romance and his lonely days were brightened by the company of young Bessie Vickery, who he had met one day on a walk.

In spite of his disappointment that The Land Fit for Heroes was just the same as it was before the war, but with fewer heroes, Albert reflected that at least he had a girlfriend, a home and a job. For others in Weatherfield, things were much worse.

From the war he had his memories, his medals and a new-found independence which was to stay with him for the rest of his life. He had one more memento from the war which was also to stay with him — a piece of floating shrapnel in his leg, which surfaced at regular intervals as a painful reminder of 1 July 1916.

Much support for the local recruiting campaign came from Jim Corbishley of the Rover's Return who, on the outbreak of war in August, draped the wall of the public bar with a Union Jack and surrounded it with pictures of Wellington, Kitchener, Gordon and even Lord Nelson, as though to give the encouragement of the nation's heroes to the Weatherfield recruiting drive. Jim had offered his own services, but at 49 he was considered, at that early stage in the war, to be too old. His son Charlie, known locally as 'Charmer' because of his way with the ladies, was accepted and proudly bore the uniform of the Lancashire Fusiliers as he became the first local man to receive his embarkation orders and to set sail for France.

Sadly, Jim had cause to regret his initial fervour as young Charlie was destined never to return to Weatherfield. He died in a Southampton hospital from wounds received on the Somme in 1916.

Sarah Bridges, a barmaid at the Rover's who had enjoyed a brief fling with Charlie, was much saddened by his loss — she had set her sights on the eligible bachelor — but was soon freed from her grief by the covert attentions of Alfie Marsh who, although not a matinée idol, did know how to show a girl a good time.

≋ THE SILENT SHAME OF MO MARSH ≋

'I don't 'ave no secrets. Me life's an open book.'

Alfie Marsh, who lived with his wife Mo at Number 1, was not a nice man. He'd acquired the tenancy of Number 1 Coronation Street by opting out of the strike at Hardcastle's Mill in 1911 and seeking favour with the mill owner, who was also the landlord. He gladly withstood the insults and brickbats hurled at him by his fellow workers as he reported for work each day and was totally unaffected by the shocked reaction of Mo to the vitriolic abuse of her once-friendly neighbours.

Poor Mo had long been a drudge who lived only to serve her beloved Alfie. His valiant stand against the strikers was not motivated by a desire to improve the lot of Mo and his household, but to ensure his promotion to foreman. The extra money gained by his new position remained strictly in Alfie's pocket.

When he had married Mo, he had done so under the impression that her father, Len Dowty, was a rich man. Len spent money freely and was a flashy dresser, who always kept a good table at their home in Inkerman Street. It was rumoured that Len actually *owned* his house and in those times home ownership was a sure sign of wealth and prosperity.

Mo Dowty, who was not unattractive but inclined to frumpishness, was astounded when man of the world Alfie came to court her, and soon succumbed to his superficial charm.

They were married in 1911 and moved in with the Dowtys as a temporary measure while Alfie, who had no intention of setting up a home without a positive donation from Len Dowty, added to his savings.

When Len died after falling down the stairs, supposedly in a drunken state, the police were called in to investigate, but could find no tangible evidence to act upon. However, tongues wagged and the finger of suspicion pointed very positively in the direction of Alfred Marsh who had always made no secret of the fact that he and Mo would inherit a substantial amount when Len died.

When the news circulated that Len Dowty had not only died virtually penniless, but had left a legacy of petty debts all over Weatherfield, his neighbours were surprised but rallied round to help his wife Louise clean his slate. No such offer came from Alfie — he even asked Louise for £2 that he claimed he'd lent to Len.

Suddenly, living with Mo's mother became a burden to Alfie and with the prospect of supporting both women, he moved out to Coronation Street after he was offered Number 1 and from then on he offered

Alfie Marsh kept terrible secrets from his wife Mo: not only did he have another wife but it was also rumoured that he had a hand in the mysterious death of Mo's father.

his mother-in-law very little time or attention.

He appeared to be making the best of what he and Mo, who cleaned the Mission in the few hours she had away from Number 1, could muster. But while Mo worked uncomplainingly, Alfie, at 49, became the headstrong young lover and ran off with Sarah Bridges, the comely barmaid from the Rover's. Sarah's qualities were obvious, but homekeeping was definitely not one of them.

Fortunately for Mo, there were no children to look after and she was able to scrape a living by doing cleaning locally. Louise Dowty died in early 1916 and with the sale of the effects from Inkerman Street and her own little income, Mo was able to keep body and soul together without outside help.

Number 1 sparkled with cleanliness and attention, and Mo was convinced that Alfie would eventually tire of Sarah, see the error of his ways and return home. She believed that, at 50, he would stop chasing after women and would welcome a return to his comfortable billet where he knew a doting wife waited to care for him.

Her dreams were ruined when a stern-faced, elderly woman knocked on the door of Number 1 and introduced herself as Mrs Sybil Marsh. She claimed to have married 'Alfred', as she referred to him, in Scarborough in 1900. She was near to 60 at least, but was well dressed and obviously had a fair bit of money. Mo realized Sybil had probably been Alfie's first step to a better life by marrying into money. Sybil told Mo she needed to track down Alfie so she could divorce him to remarry and if that meant putting the police on to him to charge him for bigamy, so be it.

Bigamy! Poor Mo suddenly saw herself as a participating criminal and she hid in the back room of Number 1, where every knock on the door sent shudders through her as she anticipated the arrival of an arresting officer. Her neighbours became quite concerned about not seeing her and it was only with Tommy Foyle, the owner of the corner shop, that she made contact as she called to make her frugal purchases late at night.

The mystery was soon cleared up when Sybil returned to the street early one morning once again to knock loudly on the door of Number 1. Poor Mo, terrified of her caller and expecting her to be accompanied by a constable, refused to open the door. Sybil was not to be silenced. She called through the letterbox that she had tracked down Alfie to Bolton, and that he had got married yet again — this time to a barmaid. She warned of serious repercussions once the police had been notified.

The whole scene was overheard by next-door neighbour, Gertie Hewitt, who lingered while washing her step taking notice of every word. She later reported the news around Coronation Street in minute detail.

Locked up in Number 1, Mo realized that not only was it the end of her dream of a new life with Alfie, but also that she saw herself as a bigamist married to a double bigamist. She felt no anger; she was convinced Alfie had been led astray, but she was so overcome with guilt and, above all fear, that there seemed no way out.

She spent the rest of the day cleaning and polishing her home. The fires were cleaned out and grates blacked, the draining board scrubbed and the

Miss Long, Sunday School teacher at the Mission of Glad Tidings, led the Whit Walks through half-deserted streets in 1916. The news received just before the procession left, that her fiancé had been killed, did not stop her from leading the local children who were in need of some normality in their lives.

plates and cups carefully hung on the dresser. No corner of the little house remained undusted, no piece of brass or copper was left unpolished.

Her task completed, she packed a small suitcase, spent a few moments looking round every room in the house and walked out into the fading daylight.

The next day, her body was found floating in the canal by market men setting up their stalls in Plank Street market. Later, her suitcase was handed in at Tile Street police station. It had been found abandoned on the Rosamund Street bridge over the canal. Inside were a nightdress, a small prayer book, a silver-framed wedding photograph and a pair of Alfie's striped pyjamas. She left no note to indicate any intention to commit suicide.

Her death was to remain a mystery that was discussed for years after. Had she jumped? Had she fallen? Or had there been another reason for her death in the unkind, rubbish-filled waters of the canal?

Alfie Marsh was never seen again and the police closed their books on a sad suicide victim, who had left as her only epitaph a house that sparkled with cleanliness and care, but that was as empty and cold as Alfie and Mo's marriage.

Emily Popplewell left Coronation Street in 1916 to serve as a nurse in France. After the war she made the country her home and married a wounded French officer.

As the war progressed, and foreign names like 'Wipers', Passchendaele and Verdun became as commonplace in conversation as Blackpool, Southport and Morecambe, the realization that the enemy were not readily capitulating to the British flag came as the casualty lists were published and the wounded heroes of the trenches were carried home to a future of pain and hopelessness.

Around Coronation Street the losses included docker Ralph Makepiece, one of the many victims of July 1916 and the Somme, who left behind an illegitimate child, Trevor Cog borne by Betty Cog. Harry Moss, Gladys Arkwright's nephew from the Vestry also fell at the Somme, much to the distress of young Ena Schofield who had been walking out with him.

One of the saddest losses was borne by the Piggotts of Number 13 who lost both their sons in one single shell burst.

Joe Buck had married Kelly Smith in March 1913. Whilst he served in the war, she lived with his parents at Number 9 along with their son Jim.

EMMA PIGGOTT — A MOTHER'S TALE

'We're the Piggotts. We're dead rough. Ask anyone. Well, I've got feelin's too. I've an 'eart. I can bleed an' all yer know.'

The Piggotts from Number 13 Coronation Street were another family who were victims of the Great War.

Fred was a foreman at Hardcastle's where Emma, his wife since 1895,

Weaver Emma Piggott's life was turned upside down by the deaths of her twin sons. Her husband's refusal to talk about the incident caused her to become depressed and withdrawn.

worked as a weaver. Even when their twin sons Robert and Victor were born in 1897, Emma continued working to ensure that her family had a relatively comfortable life amongst all the poverty that surrounded them.

Ivy Makepiece, who lived next door at Number 11 agreed to take charge of the twins, for a small consideration. She was basically a kind woman who just tried to do too much.

When she took on the boys, she had two children of a similar age and was pleased to have four young charges to occupy her days. But Alfred Makepiece, like many of his time, believed a big family to be God's will and he and Ivy produced three further little Makepieces in quick succession, despite the cramped conditions.

With seven children to look after and her small jobs, taken on to augment Alfred's earnings, she became bad tempered and strict with her charges. Her temper was worse for the Piggott boys; she often took a stick to them and scolded them frequently.

Their early experiences, when it had been just them battling against the Makepieces, bound them together and during their schooldays they always kept a certain distance from the other children. Even when they joined up in 1915 to serve with the Lancashire Fusiliers, they preferred to find their friends from outside Weatherfield. They were always together in life, and so it was in death when a stray shell landed on their dugout at the Somme.

Their mother received the dreaded yellow envelope with silent composure, but her grief was extreme. Fred's answer to the tragedy was to drown his sorrows in the Rover's, refusing even to talk to his wife of his lost sons. When Emma sought his company as a companion in grief he rebuffed her.

In desperation for some comfort she began to make enquiries about young Alice Buck from down the street, who had said that she had become pregnant after a night of passion with Victor on his embarkation leave. Alice had been the subject of much speculation as it became obvious that she was pregnant and she had come to Emma asking for money. Emma was shocked, but cynical in the light of Alice's known lack of morals and, not believing that Victor was the father, had showed her the door.

When Alice's son Ben was born, her parents couldn't cope with an extra mouth to feed and threw her out. She disappeared from the neighbourhood with her infant son, a blanket and just a few shillings that Ned Buck shoved into her hand as he shut the door in her face.

Emma was now clutching at straws and saw baby Ben as her last possible link with Victor. She spent many hours knocking on the doors of lodging houses and hostels in the vain hope of finding her grandson. By now she had convinced herself that Alice's baby *was* Victor's.

She heard that Alice had gone to London, but Emma was getting exhausted — she had neither the money nor the energy to follow her trail there. Her life had been shattered by that shell burst in France. Her precious sons, her handsome, clever young boys were not coming home. Emma was sinking mentally and physically.

She rallied each morning to dust and polish the boys' room. Somehow she managed to convince herself that Robert and Victor may not have been in the dugout and tried to convince herself that it had been two other young men who had been blown to pieces.

With the Armistice in November 1918 and still no sign of her sons, she finally gave up hope and offered little resistance to the severe bout of influenza she suffered in late 1918. She died on Christmas Eve clutching a picture of the boys, with their last Christmas card sent from Calais in 1915 sitting on the table by her bedside.

Fred was left alone to grieve. There was nothing to keep him in Weatherfield and he gladly accepted the offer from his widowed sister to go and help her run the small draper's shop she and her late husband had established near Norwich.

Soon after Fred's departure, Jim Corbishley received a postcard, addressed to him and all the neighbours, showing a sunlit meadow leading down to the riverside at Thorpe. A little cross against a row of shops in the background indicated where Alfred had finally found his solace.

Jim was impressed and pinned the card to the wall in the Snug where, for many years, the halcyon scene was admired by those retreating from the smoky atmosphere of Coronation Street.

However, not all of Weatherfield's heroes were destined to leave devastated families and to receive a posthumous accolade — Albert Tatlock returned home wounded but decorated. His close pal, Dinky Low, also returned but grief had made him a broken man.

⇲ DINKY LOW'S BRIEF HAPPINESS ⇱

'I don't know about it bein' a long way to Tipperary. All I know is it's an 'eck of a long way to Weatherfield. An' that's where the sweetest girl I know is.'

When Dinky Low was separated from Albert and Clarrie on that dreadful summer morning in 1916 on the Somme, his thoughts were solely on

Twins Robert (standing) and Victor Piggott had arrived in Coronation Street when they were five. At the age of 19 they were killed on the Somme.

Alice Buck had been desperately in love with her sweetheart Victor Piggott and had slept with him during his leave. A week after the birth of her illegitimate son Ben she was thrown out by her morally strict father Ned.

self-survival. Like all about him, he kept his head low, dived for the nearest shell hole and prayed for his life. With shells and whizzbangs overhead and deadly machine gun fire pecking the ground only inches above him, Dinky began to believe his last hours had really arrived.

He'd gone over the top with Albert and Clarrie at 7.30 am, looking forward to the easy advance forward to occupy enemy lines that they had been promised, but minutes later the German machine gunners opened fire and Dinky was cowering in a crater with his two companions stranded somewhere behind him.

He was unable to move forward because of the machine gun fire and to retreat would have meant his facing possible charges of cowardice or even desertion and ending up in front of a firing squad. The chain of command was broken and Dinky could not raise his head without provoking yet another machine gun burst. He decided to wait for orders but keep alert to any possible counter-attack from the German lines.

His thoughts went back to Albert and Clarrie who had been right beside him for about 100 yards and then, suddenly, gone to ground. Were they safe or had they fallen with the first wave of infantrymen to come under attack?

Unbelievably, even right in the thick of this massive carnage, even with machine guns, whizzbangs and cannon shells everywhere, Dinky's thoughts went back to those lazy summer afternoons of 1914 and his sweetheart Madge Narkey. Madge had been Dinky's sweetheart since they were at school together and had been one of the few girls privileged to join the Wheelers on their travels. From time to time, his thoughts were interrupted by the bloody and tragic events around him but in those dramatic hours he was able to relive that last happy summer and resolved to marry his Madge at the first opportunity.

Eventually, darkness fell and Dinky managed to make his way back to base where he eagerly sought news of his pals. There was no news, and after a frugal meal, and a cup of tea, he and some others who had become separated and returned to Command set off again over the open space that separated them from the Germans. Albert and Clarrie had obviously been shot and Dinky was now all alone with only himself to think about.

He did just that, and good luck favoured him throughout the rest of the futile campaign. He made a good account of himself and by late 1917 he had been promoted to sergeant and received his CO's permission to return home on compassionate leave to marry his girlfriend Madge on 3 November 1917.

They had written regularly ever since he left Weatherfield for France, and in spite of the communications problem, Dinky had proposed marriage and been accepted by post.

On arriving at Weatherfield, Dinky's first call was to Jubilee Terrace where he anticipated a warm welcome from Madge and her family but not a meeting-up with Albert Tatlock, whom he had last seen over a year ago and presumed to be dead. Albert, with his lance-jack's stripe gleaming with blanco, was sitting in the Narkey's kitchen waiting for him.

Dinkie Low and Madge Narky had grown up together in Jubilee Terrace. The young sweethearts had also worked together until he signed up for the Fusiliers in 1914.

PIGGOT

FAMILY BUTCHERS
20 Rosamund Street

Piggott's flourished during the war when the locals boycotted Fleeshman's, the other local butcher, because of its Germanic name. Wilfred Piggott put up his prices and the public paid the cost of patriotism.

It was a joyous meeting all round and even the fate of Clarrie Ross, which he learned from a sad-faced Albert, did not dampen his anticipation of his wedding the next day. Albert agreed to be best man, even though he was still limping badly from his leg wound and needed a stick.

After the wedding ceremony, the small party returned to the Flying Horse where Cissy Ross, Clarrie's widowed mother, had laid on a modest reception of sandwiches, soft drinks and two crates of ale. By now Dinky, like Albert, had graduated from dandelion and burdock to beer and wine and, although by no means real drinkers, they enjoyed Mrs Ross' hospitality to the full. The evening ended in a sing-song as Albert and Dinky recalled the songs of the trenches.

Eventually Dinky and Madge's 'Long, Long Trail' wound as far as their new home at Number 1 Coronation Street, and they enjoyed their first and only night as Mr and Mrs Low. Their honeymoon, next day, consisted of a walk round the Red Rec and a slap-up tea at Trumper's Tea Rooms in Clarence Street.

Dinky was due back with his unit on the following day and was seen off at the tram stop by Madge and Albert. Albert promised to be back 'over there' quite soon and Madge, tearfully but bravely, kissed goodbye to her husband of only one day. Little did she know that she would never see him again.

On the home front, Madge continued working at Hardcastle's Mill in spite of discovering she was pregnant. Dinky, now back at the front and reunited with Albert, received the news of Madge's pregnancy by field telegram and for the first time in either of their lives, he and Albert got drunk as they supped wine from metal cups in their dug-out.

Dinky was looking forward to the end of the war and a return to his new home, wife and baby when a letter arrived from home. Madge had clearly written when extremely distressed and exhausted, having given birth prematurely to a stillborn child. One week later, Dinky's sadness was complete when another telegram brought the worst possible news — his beloved wife Madge had also been taken only days after her ordeal.

What was left of the war was still to be enacted, but Dinky went through the motions as though in a daze. His grief gave way to wild aggression and when danger beckoned he was always first to answer the call. He led very much from the front and Albert, who was mindful of his own safety, watched with his heart in his mouth, as Dinky undertook the most dangerous missions. But luck favoured Dinky and he and Albert returned home together, unscathed.

On the surface, Dinky was the decorated hero home from the war, but inside there was only emptiness and pain. Weatherfield, the companion of his thoughts in those dreadful days on the Somme, was now a place of ghosts and unfulfilled promises. Shortly after arriving back, he decided he needed to make a clean break away from Weatherfield.

Before leaving for London, he had one last kindness to bestow on Albert who'd been his playmate, pal and comrade-at-arms, all in such a short time. He negotiated with the mill to allow Albert who was now engaged to

Bessie, to take over Number 1 and, like Dinky and Madge, they moved in on their wedding day. He left in 1919, dapper as ever and apparently filled with ambition and hope.

Dinky was gone, but Albert was left with a reminder that was to stay with him for the rest of his life. A brief note told Albert and Bessie that 'Chippy' Foster would be calling shortly to build a sideboard that Dinky had picked out of a catalogue from Kendall-Milne. It was to be copied by Chippy and then assembled in the room, as it was too big to pass down the narrow hallway of Number 1. He and Madge had chosen it on their last day together.

It had been paid for a long time ago and Dinky wished Albert and Bessie to have it as a belated wedding gift. Dinky's sideboard was always to remain the prize possession of Number 1.

☀

The area's first national hero was Lieutenant Geoffrey Warbeck of the RFC from Oakhill who forced a German Albatross plane to the ground by ramming it after his own Sopwith Pup had been badly damaged, and then had the temerity to arrest the German flier at gunpoint, behind his own lines, and lead him back to British custody. For this achievement Lt Warbeck received a bar for his DFC awarded for an earlier aerial victory over Mons. Sadly, he did not survive and was killed in the very last week of the war in a flying accident in Mesopotamia.

The Royal Navy and the Merchant Navy both provided their heroes and Able Seaman Walter Rough and his brother Teddy, from Omdurman Street both distinguished themselves as brave gunners at the Battle of Jutland in May 1916.

When the liner *Lusitania* was sunk in May 1915, among its victims were Percy and Thomas Lewthwaite, a father and son from Crimea Street, who both served on board as stewards. Their bodies were never recovered but the whole neighbourhood turned out for their touching memorial service at St Mary's church.

Another marine tragedy occcurred in June 1916, when Lord Kitchener's ship was torpedoed in the Scapa Flow, much to the shock of the British nation. The War Secretary had become the very symbol of British patriotism as his stern features and pointing finger informed all eligible recruits that 'Your Country needs you'. His death was felt by all in the area and schools were closed, factories shut down and funereal drapes placed over windows when the devastating news came through. The Mission of Glad Tidings was the scene of a sad gathering as the Coronation Street community got together to offer up prayers for his eternal salvation.

Joyce Shaw served as barmaid at the Rover's Return from 1916 to the end of the war. She looked upon the work as her contribution to the War Effort.

On the home front, much was as before; the poor still struggled from day to day and many of the children were still underfed and shabby, but strangely the loss of the main bread-winner in families, did not add to the poverty, as the jobs left vacant by soldiering menfolk were now filled by their women.

Following the *Lusitania* disaster, a massive wave of anti-German feeling ran rampant in the Weatherfield area and shops with names which even suggested their proprietor might be of German descent were starved of custom and sometimes damaged as the casualty lists were published in the newspapers and the dreaded knock of the telegram cyclist brought news of another tragedy to an anxious household.

Even people with a long-established British family background, who were unfortunate enough to possess a foreign sounding name, were treated with suspicion. The Schofields of Inkerman Street often had quite a bit of explaining to do.

One shop that had little to worry about was the fish and chip shop established by Olive Thurgood in her front parlour in Victoria Street. It had proved to be so successful that Eli Thurgood had left his job at the mill to join her and they had turned the premises into a sparse but extremely popular place to get tasty fried fish, pies and chips. The dark evenings of the war, with fuel shortages and, often, only candle power for light were frequently lifted by a visit to Thurgoods to bring back a piping hot, newspaper-wrapped supper.

Olive died just before the Christmas of 1915 and their son Ronnie Thurgood was killed while serving in France in 1916, but Eli soldiered on in the shop with assistance easily acquired from the solitary and lonely housewives seeking to earn a little extra money. In 1918, he sold out to Solomon Jackson, shortly after purchasing the freehold for £120 from Mabel Hardcastle, and moved to a new life in Canada.

Meanwhile, at the corner shop in Coronation Street, bachelor Tommy Foyle was finding life difficult as the shortages of war eventually led to official rationing. This resulted in acrimony when customers of long standing were refused their favourite foods and left Tommy feeling like the villain of the piece.

It was fortunate for Tommy that his very noticeable limp, caused by a badly ulcerated leg, left his customers in no doubt that even as a man in his mid-twenties, he was an unsuitable candidate for war service.

To be a conscientious objector in these times of war, whatever the reason, was to court the scorn and sometimes open hostility of the more outspoken members of society who, usually in no danger of serving themselves, saw fit to condemn and to call cowards all young men not in uniform. The White Feather became the symbol of cowardice, and was frequently presented to eligible-looking men in civilian clothes — sometimes, even to servicemen on leave.

SID HAYES — THE PEACE LOVING SAMARITAN

'The Good Book tells me to turn the other cheek, what does it tell you?'

The day Sid Hayes was handed a white feather as everybody around him was celebrating the great Armistice of 1918 was to live with him for the rest of his life.

Post Office worker Sid lived at Number 5 Coronation Street with his wife Alice and children, Ada and Fred.

As a lay preacher, regular mission worker and genuine do-gooder, Sid was highly respected in Coronation Street. The woes of the early 1900s when there was so much poverty, disease and overcrowding, left many in Weatherfield feeling hopeless and in despair. But Sid was always a friend they could turn to for counselling if not for money.

Lay preacher Sid Hayes found he could not condone a war and yet still preach peace and humility. His refusal to sign up led to a four-year prison sentence.

Alice Hayes moved into Number 5 on her wedding day. As the day was fine she felt sure her stay in Coronation Street would be a happy one.

While his wife Alice turned out regularly to play the organ at St Thomas' Church, Sid spread the word of God to the needy. His sermons preached harmony and love of one's neighbours and few families in his 'parish' did not benefit at some time from his continual efforts.

At the outbreak of war in 1914, Sid was faced with the dilemma of joining in the fervour of support for the bloody conflict to come, or following his natural instincts towards pacifism and to preach against it.

He chose a middle line, neither opposing nor supporting the war, but his conscience would not allow him to enlist. Many did not enlist, for far different and less moral reasons than Sid, but in the public eye of Weatherfield he was lumped in with the rest and labelled a 'conchie'.

Possibly in those early days of the war he could, like others of his beliefs, have opted to serve as a medic or stretcher bearer but, to Sid, anyone in uniform who was involved in the war was guilty of releasing the fatal shot.

Until the volunteers ran out (and there were many from Weatherfield), Sid was able to continue his good work on the Home Front. He was still able to carry on in spite of the coolness with which he was now received in some quarters. But bereaved families, sometimes facing the loss of all their menfolk, did not turn away from his help and kind words.

Then came conscription for all able bodied men, and Sid, in his thirty-ninth year, received the call to arms. He refused and was imprisoned. Not only his 'parishioners' but also his family suffered from his absence. Alice was forced to eke out an existence without Sid's wage, but was surprised and relieved to receive a small sum of money that his colleagues at the Post Office had collected on her behalf.

In 1916, Sid learned that his young son Fred had died at two years old from diphtheria. Behind bars in the cold and severe conditions of his Dartmoor prison, Sid's social spirit was still not dampened and in the company of his fellow civil offenders he was still enthusiastic about spreading the Word of God.

With the Allied victory in sight, Sid was released in October 1918 and returned to a household still tainted by his reputation. He was accepted back at the Post Office but his immediate superior, Captain Warboys, who had been invalided out of the army earlier that year, made it clear that future promotion was unlikely.

The Armistice of 11 November was followed by a Victory Parade along Rosamund Street that contained a body of men from the Lancashire Fusiliers — all heroes, and many well-known to the people in Weatherfield.

As some of the Weatherfield lads marched past the Rover's, Sid joined in the recognition of their efforts, clapping and cheering as loudly as anyone. He applauded their brave survival, not their conquests.

A tap on his shoulder caused him to turn round and he was confronted by Ivy Makepiece who had obviously just emerged in a drunken state from the Rover's.

Ostentatiously, she thrust on him a white feather, then slapped his face in front of all Sid's friends and neighbours. Sadly, he looked after her retreating figure and thought to himself: 'They will never understand.'

As the conflict neared its end and the news of peace from the front became more of a certainty, especially after the arrival of the American GIs, a new air of hope spread through Weatherfield.

Many had perished for the cause, but many had survived and were coming home. There were boys who'd become men in one battle; weaklings who'd become strong from the example of others, and the hopeless unemployed who'd come home with newly acquired skills learned in the field, with which to forge a new, better life for themselves and their families.

One notable change in Weatherfield was when the Rover's Return public house, named to commemorate Philip Ridley's heroic deeds at Spion Kop, lost its apostrophe and was renamed the Rovers Return to record the heroic deeds of all Weatherfield's rovers now returned to the fold.

The Victory Parade along Rosamund Street in November 1919 was the greatest local gathering of all time. Thousands of people packed the pavements of Weatherfield's main thoroughfare. Bands played, soldiers marched, flags waved and people cheered. They cheered the return of their loved ones, the victory of good over evil and the undoubted dawn of a new, brighter era.

Weatherfield entered 1919 with a celebration unequalled in living memory. The age of peace and prosperity was surely about to begin in the Land Fit for Heroes.

Ned and Sarah Buck ran a funeral service from their home at Number 9 Coronation Street. Whilst Sarah laid out the dead, Ned used his carpentry skill to produce cheap coffins.

CHAPTER 4

1918-1930: THE BLACK BOTTOM YEARS

The Alhambra Ballroom, Weatherfield, where the flappers and dandies would parade in their Sunday best every Saturday night to enjoy what was for most the highlight of the week.

THE BUNTING THAT had been strung up from lamp posts and windows lay limp and dusty in the gutters the week after the end of war jubilation. The street parties, which had lasted a weekend were soon over and the people of Weatherfield waited to see their men return.

The Weatherfield lads returned home not as celebrating, victorious champions, breasts ablaze with medals, but as tired, battle-scarred invalids, who had often been affected both physically and mentally. They returned to a town where their women folk had taken over the manual jobs and had proved successful in doing them. After a brief period of joyous reunion with families glad to see their loved ones back home alive, the men found jobs hard to come by. Women were cheaper to employ than men and many now enjoyed working for a living. The returning hero found he had come back to a hard, cold world where the streets were lined with other soldiers anxiously seeking employment.

Many did not return at all. Each street in Weatherfield mourned the passing of a son. Families like the Corbishleys and the Piggotts left the houses, which held too many memories, and moved on. With Charlie Corbishley dead in a Southampton hospital from injuries inflicted in the trenches, his mother Nellie had found herself viewing all the young men who drank in the Rovers with fury; why hadn't one of them died instead of her Charlie? Her husband Jim, fearing she was going to suffer a breakdown, gave up the tenancy on the pub and the couple moved away to Little Hayfield. Their housekeeper of nine years, Pearl Crapper, happily moved with them.

Some of the men that did return, like Albert Tatlock, were destined to a much happier future.

⫷ BESSIE VICKERY FINDS HER MAN ⫸

'They say the war is over. We won. We were victorious. I say they're wrong. They know nothing of the real war. The war which nobody talks about. Their war may be over, but our war still goes on, day and night.'

Elizabeth Mary Vickery became an orphan at the tender age of seven in 1911. After her guardian, an elderly maiden aunt, died, Elizabeth entered service. She was fourteen at the time and was employed as an under-house-maid to a Mr Thatcher's household in Bury, Lancashire. Bury was Elizabeth's home town and she was glad not to have to leave it. Her fellow servants shortened her name to Bessie as they thought is suited her. The name stuck and for the rest of her life Elizabeth was always known as Bessie.

Bessie spent most of her six years below stairs dodging the cook's hard slaps and vicious temper and the master's wandering hands. Mr Thatcher had a reputation as a womaniser and Bessie soon made sure she was never left alone in a room with him. Each Sunday she attended chapel at a local Baptist service, which was held especially for servants. She only had one afternoon off a week and this time she usually spent walking in the park.

Bessie Tatlock moved into Number .1 in October 1919. She hardly knew her new husband Albert, but they had plenty of chance to get to know each other in their forty-year marriage.

It was during one of those walks that she had met Albert Tatlock. The war had started and he was receiving military training in Bury. Bessie was nineteen at the time and she'd never had an admirer, never been kissed.

Albert shyly kissed her before his regiment left in late 1915 to fight in France. She had sneaked off duty to wave him off at the station. She had shared the excitement he felt at the adventures he was going to experience and the honours he hoped to receive on his glorious return.

18 October 1919, Bessie and Albert's wedding day, turned out to be a dull, cloudy Saturday. They had got married in Bury and the train journey back from Bury to Manchester had been slow and the tram ride on to Weatherfield was even slower. Bessie had never travelled to this town before, but her first reaction was that it was much like Bury, as were the inhabitants. The industrial towns of this time seemed to breed the same poorly dressed, depressed-looking inhabitants. Bessie had married Albert, her war hero, in the Baptist chapel of her home town and she had then happily left her job and the place of her birth. A job had been found for her at the local mill and she was to start on Monday 20th. Her new home at Number 1 Coronation Street was situated in the shadow of the mill itself. The huge mill building prevented any sunlight from reaching the house, which was situated next to a noisy pub. Still, at least they had a home and jobs; many war veterans were left to beg in the streets, often hobbling along minus an arm or leg, which had been lost in the battles of the French fields.

The war had changed Albert, he was no longer the laughing, good-humoured man that she had first known. He never talked to her about his war experiences, but she knew from the way he cried out in his sleep that he was still suffering terrible nightmares. On their wedding night his cries had woken her from her sleep. He did not wake up, but he was shaking and sweating profusely, as he called out names and cried and screamed. Not knowing what to do, she just held him to her, trying to comfort him. The nightmares continued for many years and Bessie grew to accept them as part of Albert. The quiet man she had married put up a front each day, to her and the outside world. He was more a companion than a passionate lover, but Bessie accepted this. Each night he would cling to her, weeping in his sleep and she would kiss his brow and ease him back to a peaceful slumber.

Four-year-old Ida Leathers won the bouncing baby contest held at the Mission of Glad Tidings to celebrate the new decade.

Those men who were in employment found some of the local mill owners were cutting their wages to nearly the same level as their female colleagues. Those who complained were quickly sacked. Some men, like Thomas Hewitt, kept quiet; he was grateful just to be home and in work. By February 1921 the number of unemployed topped one million, 368,000 of whom were ex-servicemen. As the numbers increased, the Government raised unemployment benefit from 15 shillings to 18 shillings a week.

≥ THOMAS ENDS A FAMILY FEUD ≤

'I'm sick of fightin', sick of battles and war and strife. Life shouldn't be like that. Not all the time. The time's come for peace, for God's sake.'

The Great War had left Weatherfield with a surplus of single women. Over a thousand young men had been killed on the battlefields of France and Belgium, and those who returned found themselves eagerly sought after.

The Makepiece girls at Number 11 Coronation Street lay in bed together each night whispering about the young men who had caught their eye that day. Sandwiched between her sisters, Lil and Susie, Mary Makepiece drifted off to sleep dreaming about the man she had fallen for — Thomas Hewitt. Not that she'd ever confess to her family that she liked Thomas; she was scared to because he was a Hewitt and a sworn enemy of her family.

The feud had started before the Great War. No one could remember exactly how it started but it was something to do with Samuel Hewitt from Number 3 accepting promotion at Hardcastle's mill when Alfred Makepiece was next in line for the job. Alfred had expected his drinking mate Samuel to step down in favour of him and was shocked when he didn't. Furthermore, in his new position as weaving shed foreman, Samuel removed Alfred's wife Ivy from the shed for spreading malicious gossip about him and replaced her with his own wife Gertie. Alfred and Samuel were both dead now, but for the last twelve years the families had been having rows with each other at the slightest excuse.

Thomas Hewitt returned from the Great War to fight a new battle at home — to marry his sweetheart in the face of family opposition.

Mary could never forget that frightening day in May 1917 when the news reached Gertie Hewitt that her mother had dropped dead in the Bakers Lane workhouse that all the family tried to forget about. Whilst Gertie made hurried arrangements for a cheap burial, Ivy Makepiece led the local women in their condemnation of a woman who could let her own mother die so shamefully. Gertie was not proud of herself and tried to ignore the snide comments of her neighbours. That night a drunken Ned Buck, too old to be fighting abroad, showed his contempt for Gertie by smashing her front parlour window with a brick.

Ned stumbled back into his house at Number 9 and when Gertie came out to investigate the crash, she found the only person in the street to be Ivy Makepiece. The next morning Gertie summoned Ivy to her front door, and, before she could do anything, she threw the contents of her chamber pot into her face. For a second Ivy was too shocked to move, then she sprang onto Gertie and the two fought like dogs in the street, rolling around on the cobbles together.

The screams of the fighting women brought all the residents out onto the street. Flo and Molly Hewitt tried to help their mother but found themselves being set upon by the Makepiece girls. Jim Corbishley was sent for and he came rushing from the Rovers Return with a bucket of water which he threw over the women. The shock of the cold water made them both stop fighting. Ivy picked herself up from the gutter and marched passed the onlookers into her house. Gertie cheered in triumph, thinking herself to be the winner, but Ivy returned brandishing the most sacred of books — the rent book. Waving it in the air for all the neighbours to see, Ivy showed off the fact that her book was up to date; she had no arrears as she always paid her rent on time. She challenged Gertie to bring her rent book out for all to see. Gertie knew she was beaten; she struggled with the rent and was often in arrears, a fact she had tried to hide. Somehow Ivy had found out. Gertie tried to remain dignified as she walked into her home, but the Makepiece family stood outside and jeered her.

Even now, after all their close-knit community had suffered during the war, the two families still ignored each other. Gertie had tried to make peace in 1916 when Ivy's son Ralph was killed on the Somme but grief made Ivy bitter and she turned on Gertie as her own son was still alive.

Thomas Hewitt had returned from the Great War unscathed, both physically and mentally. Unlike many of his friends he suffered no shell shock from the trenches and settled down quickly to life back in Weatherfield. Although many of his childhood friends were no longer around, Thomas found little had changed in his home town. One thing had changed dramatically though; he had gone off to war as little more that a lad and had returned a man. For the first time in his twenty years Thomas began to notice the women and girls he had grown up with.

Thomas had never liked the feud with his neighbours and did not think it was a good enough reason not to court Mary Makepiece. He could tell she liked him; no other girl blushed like she did when he tipped his cap at her, and he had seen her lingering in the back alley hoping to catch a glimpse of him. He made sure she was never disappointed.

For a few weeks Mary was happy to play games with Thomas but the knowledge that he was one of the few eligible young men around in Weatherfield prompted her into overcoming her shyness and making a move. Taking her sister Lil for protection, Mary ventured into the Rovers Return one night. Neither girl had entered the pub before and they found the smoky bar full of men who viewed them with interest, but also suspicion. New landlady, Mary Diggins, beckoned them into the Snug and asked them what they wanted to drink. Thomas had been standing at the bar and had witnessed their shy entrance. He understood at once why the two girls had built up the courage to come in and felt it was time for him to do his bit. Walking into the Snug he paid for the drinks and exchanged a warm smile with Mary.

Gertie Hewitt refused to speak to Thomas for three months when she knew he was taking Mary out. Ivy Makepiece threatened to lock Mary in her room on her wedding day, but neither took any notice of their bitter parents. Both pointed out that they needed no one's consent to marry, but they would like their families' blessings. Despite all the happy thoughts of her forthcoming marriage, the hostility she received at home greatly upset Mary. Thomas found her crying in the street one night after her mother had called her a slut and he decided enough was enough.

Thomas cornered his mother, Gertie, and Ivy Makepiece in the street. Neither wanted to be drawn into conversation, but the sight of Thomas physically restraining Gertie from moving amused Ivy so much that she stopped to listen to what he had to say. He did not waste words. He told them what he had experienced in the trenches. He shared with them all his pain and distress and told them how so many of his young friends' lives had been wasted. He told them he had lost years of his youth, which he would never have again. He told them he was sick of battles and conflict and that he deserved some happiness and peace. He then told them, in no uncertain terms, that with or without their blessings he was going to marry Mary.

The following day was a Sunday. The chapel worshippers were startled to see Gertie Hewitt sitting together with Ivy Makepiece with their best clothes on in the main hall. At the end of the service they rose and left the chapel together. The congregation stared after the retreating pair. What was going to happen? The two women walked together to William Fazackery's house in Crimea Street and returned to Coronation Street arm in arm, chattering away as if they were the best of friends. They summoned the two lovers, Thomas and Mary, and gave them a key. In answer to their puzzled looks, Ivy told them that they'd need somewhere to live after they were married; she and Gertie had gone to secure for them the tenancy of Number 7 Coronation Street. If they were going to be married the two mothers were determined to have them close by to keep their eyes on them!

Mary Makepiece was prepared to turn her back on her family for the sake of the man she loved.

Food shortages after the Great War led to steep price increases in the local shops and the recession forced many shopkeepers out of business. Tommy Foyle, the owner of the corner shop on Coronation Street refused credit to everyone except his neighbours in the street. After refusing credit to a Mawdsley Street woman, Tommy had his shop window broken by her angry husband. In Rosamund Street, Thomas Swindley was forced to close half of his haberdashery emporium and sack two of his staff. He had made an effort to employ ex-servicemen and felt very angry that he was now forcing them onto the breadline.

THE NEAR RUIN OF TOMMY FOYLE

Tommy Foyle took over the corner shop in 1914. He would remain there until his death in 1945.

'Open that door and look for anyone decent. You'll have a long search, I can tell you.'

The big advantage of marrying Elsie Castleway wasn't particularly her good looks or fun sense of humour, it was the fact that she had no incumbent family. She moved into the shop with one new suitcase and a flimsy hat box and that was all. There were no brothers, sisters, aunts, cousins or even a mother. Elsie came from Ashton and she entered Tommy Foyle's life quite alone.

Tommy had been a widower for three years, his vivacious wife Lil having died from bronchitis during the winter of 1927. The memory of Lil's funeral still sent shivers down Tommy's spine; they had all been there, the entire clan. When he married Lil, in 1923, the neighbours had tried to warn him about the consequences of marrying a Makepiece. No amount of warnings could have prepared him for the next four years when he found himself grafted onto the biggest extended family in the Weatherfield area.

The horde of Makepieces living at Number 11 Coronation Street were only a small part; the family was one of the oldest in town and seemed to have a foothold in every street and public house. As the sun shone brightly on his wedding day, Tommy had no idea of the implications of marrying into this clan.

Ivy Makepiece might have looked like a sweet, docile old lady, but under her bonnet a mighty brain worked overtime plotting the destinies of each of her children, and hunting down suitable partners for them. It was to Ivy's frustration that most of her children had chosen their own, highly unsuitable, mates. Her daughter Vi had married local rogue and good-for-nothing Jack Todd; Mary was now living at Number 7 with her Hewitt husband and Susie had her eyes on married Billy Chad from Number 3. Even her best-loved son Ralph had rebelled — he had fathered an illegitimate son by Betty Cog and had lived with a teacher in Jubilee Terrace. She had decided that on balance it was probably a good thing his body lay buried in the French trenches. At least she had been able to 'guide' Lil into marrying the suitable Mr Foyle, shopkeeper and chairman of the local temperance society.

After a brief honeymoon in the Isle of Man, Tommy Foyle soon discovered what marriage to a Makepiece was going to cost him. Lil was a willing shop assistant and a loving wife. She was highly spirited at times, which had its advantages, but was also somewhat in awe of her husband. Little did Tommy know that Ivy Makepiece had coached her daughter thoroughly. As soon as Tommy began to question the Makepieces' high credit bill, Lil would turn on all her charms and Tommy would end up feeling it was a privilege to have Ivy and her clan owing him money. It did not stop with just the Coronation Street Makepieces; Lil's relatives seemed to come from everywhere and Tommy's slate book soon carried names of people from all over Weatherfield. Every now and again the clan would pay their debts, but for the majority of the four years he was married to Lil, Tommy faced near bankruptcy every week.

The strain of not wanting to upset his lovely wife or antagonise her large, well-built uncles, who all seemed to be dockers, took its toll on Tommy's health. He suffered many sleepless nights and the strain made him short of breath and gave him chest pains. After Lil's tragic death from bronchitis, Tommy's mourning was interrupted by Ivy and the clan still claiming their credit at the shop. Ivy, fearful of losing her hold on her local shop, tried to interest Tommy in marrying one of her nieces, while secretly cursing Susie for running off with Billy Chad. Tommy showed unusual strength of character by telling Ivy that he was so devastated by Lil's death that it would be a long time before he could ever consider marrying again.

The month after Lil died Tommy discovered the one thing that his mother-in-law feared most in life. He had been admiring his new window display one morning when Ivy Makepiece came running from Rosamund Street, screaming and waving her arms in the air. Her heavy skirt and coat prevented her from actually sprinting, but even so the sixty-year-old was moving very fast. As she hurried towards her house Tommy saw a mongrel dog following her. It had a pronounced limp, was short and stocky and looked as if it had been dipped in tar. Tommy thought it was the most beautiful creature he had ever seen. Ivy Makepiece might have been petrified of dogs, but Tommy Foyle certainly wasn't. As Ivy flung open her front door and disappeared upstairs, still screaming, Tommy held out his hand to the stray dog and it happily licked him. It had no collar and looked near to starvation. Tommy took it into the shop and gave it some food, which it ate hungrily.

Ill-educated Lil Makepiece willingly went along with her mother's plans to marry her off; she had nothing to lose.

Growler the dog was a regular sight as he sat in the open doorway of Foyle's grocery shop.

Larry Buck (below), invalided in the war, married Avis Grundy (above) in May 1921. Their house soon rang with children's voices when Avis gave birth to twins, Lucy and Ian in 1923.

The news that Tommy had taken in the vicious hound soon reached Ivy. Christened 'Growler' by his new master, the dog happily took up residence on the shop floor on a rag rug that Lil had made. Once he was fed and groomed he turned out to be quite harmless and enjoyed the company of everyone who came in and out of the shop. What Tommy revelled in was the fact that Ivy never ventured into his shop again and fortunately the rest of the Makepiece clan followed her example.

The only worry Tommy had upon marrying Elsie Castleway was that she and Growler may not hit it off. He needn't have worried; the dog recognized Elsie as an important person in Tommy's life and duly gave her all the love and affection she rightly deserved.

In 1933, three years after his marriage to Elsie, and six since Ivy had last given him her custom, Tommy found Growler dead in the gutter after a delivery van driver had mistakenly reversed over him. The much-loved dog was buried under a flag-stone in the shop's yard. The stone had hardly been replaced when Tommy heard the shop's bell jingling. Going to serve, Tommy found the customer was Ivy. She was now all alone at Number 11 as her family had deserted her. Without a word of greeting, Ivy produced a long shopping list and asked if her credit was still good. Tommy was speechless, but he had to admire her cheek.

Retired police sergeant George Diggins took over at the Rovers Return Inn in July 1919. His jovial wit and general good humour soon won him many friends amongst the regulars and his wife Mary pleased the local ladies by serving them in the Public Bar as well as the Snug. Most of the women still drank in the Snug however, finding the Public too smoky. To celebrate the 50th anniversary of the August bank holiday, in 1921, George organized a street outing to Blackpool. After setting off at 9am, the travellers eventually saw the sea at 3pm, due to traffic and train hold-ups. However they all swore they'd not have missed the experience for anything. Larry Buck from Number 9 took advantage of the trip to propose to his young love, mill worker Avis Grundy. She happily accepted and they were married two months later at the Mission of Glad Tidings. Playing the organ at the service was Ena Sharples, who herself had only been married for just over a year. Ena had struck up a friendship with Mission caretaker Gladys Arkwright and always helped her to set out the chairs for each meeting.

Ena's friend Minnie Carlton (later Caldwell) hitched a lift all the way to London in September 1921 to catch a glimpse of her cinema hero Charlie Chaplin. Chaplin was visiting his home country and Minnie refused to let the opportunity be wasted. In the end, she did see her favourite star, but was disappointed to discover that he was so short. Returning home she made the decision to transfer her

Ena Schofield wore a borrowed gown to marry Alfred Sharples in 1920. After the ceremony she walked from the Mission to St Mary's cemetery where she laid her bouquet on the grave of her Uncle William, who had died just a few days before.

affections to the better looking Rudolf Valentino. Minnie and Ena were regular attenders at the new Bijou cinema, built next to Hardcastle's Mill on Rosamund Street. All over Weatherfield picture palaces were being built. The economy improved and people found they had some money to spend in their free time. Whilst their husbands went to drink in the pubs, women sat enthralled through reels of film featuring Valentino, Douglas Fairbanks and the divine Gish sisters. Flo Hewitt at Number 3 Coronation Street had just grown her hair to the required length to have it styled like Lillian Gish, when suddenly the craze was for everyone to have their hair cut into short bobs.

◁ MINNIE SETTLES DOWN ▷

'I know folk think I'm simple. What I say to them is that I'd rather be simple and 'ave my pleasures than know everything and be miserable, like Ena.'

Minnie Carlton did not want to marry. However, bullied by her mother and her best friend Ena, she finally walked down the aisle with Armistead Caldwell in 1925.

While many of the areas of Weatherfield were undergoing redevelopment, the housing on the east side of the railway viaduct, virtually a hundred years old, represented all that was misery for the inhabitants living in the slum conditions. Many of the houses in the streets and lanes had been condemned as uninhabitable at the turn of the century and yet, 30 years on, the residents were still expected to go on living there.

At 14b Palmerston Street, the sound of crying babies, women arguing and the clopping of the clogs against cobbles was softened by the ticking of the 35 clocks that hung on every space of wall. They had been Bob Carlton's pride and joy and the sound each one made reminded his widow Amy of a different aspect of his character. The clocks themselves had no great value; Bob had found most of them himself and had spent hours lovingly restoring them to their former workings, but to Amy they were priceless.

Minnie Carlton viewed her father's clocks without any feelings of sentiment. She enjoyed watching the one with the bronze lady who struck a bell in her hand each hour, but the rest she could easily manage without. She would have preferred the walls to have been covered with pictures of different cats. Cats were Minnie's big passion. She did not own one herself but regularly spent part of her wages on titbits for many of the local strays.

The relationship between mother and daughter had never been very good. Amy found the girl slow on the uptake and too given to daydreaming. This she blamed on the bang on the head her elder daughter Lettie had accidentally given Minnie when she was a baby. She also disapproved of the way Minnie seemed happy to tag along with many unsavoury boys but never formed a permanent relationship. Amy still remembered with horror the weekend Minnie had spent in Southport with that scoundrel Billy Roos. Then there was the way Michael O'Flaerty from across the way had gained her a post at Greenhalgh's dye works 'for services rendered'. Amy often wondered what Minnie had had to do to get the job as there had been a queue of thirty girls in front of her. Yet it was impossible to cast tiny, timid Minnie in the role of temptress. But now, at last, the worry of looking after Minnie finally was to be lifted from her. It had taken 27 years, but Amy was about to see the last of her girls walk down the aisle.

They had met at the Band of Hope in early 1920 where Armistead Caldwell operated the Magic Lantern, under the beady eye of lay preacher Sid Hayes. The show was presented at the Mission of Glad Tidings on Coronation Street, for the under sixteens. Minnie used to enjoy standing at the back, watching the lantern slides and listening to Mr Hayes lecture on the evils of drink. It was during the society's 1920 Christmas treat for the children, when there was a special tea laid on at the Mission, that Armistead proposed to her. She had turned him down, rather candidly, on the grounds that, as a railway shunter, he always smelt of oil.

That had been five years ago. Since then Minnie had left Greenhalgh's dyeworks to work in the weaving shed at Hardcastle's Mill. She had four looms to operate, alongside her old school friend Ena Sharples. The noise the machinery made was deafening to both the friends, but Minnie still preferred it to the ticking and chiming that echoed throughout her home. As the time approached for her to leave the two tiny rooms she had known all her life, she felt no sadness, only the joy of knowing that a house in the slightly better placed Jubilee Terrace awaited her.

Minnie had no firm idea why she was marrying Armistead — it was probably the fact that he had persevered so long with wooing her. Any way, no one else had ever bothered to ask for her hand. She still found Armistead dull and too serious, but, at least, now that he was a railway foreman he no longer smelt of oil. Everyone said they made a good couple; his steadfastness complemented her inability to settle to anything. Minnie did not really want to marry anyone, but the thought of growing old as 'an old maid' and living with her mother was even less appealing.

As she walked up the aisle, contemplating how mundane her life was going to be from now on, Minnie had no idea that she had her maid of honour, Ena Sharples, to thank for any future happiness she might have. When solid, reliable, dull Armistead had begged Ena to leave her husband and run off with him, Ena had firmly refused. Although flattered by his attention and the thought that at least one other

Armistead Caldwell's marriage to Minnie only lasted ten years before his early death in 1935. When she discovered she could not bear children, Minnie ran off rather than face him. He borrowed a horse and cart to catch her and drag her home.

man desired her, Ena had advised Armistead to put thoughts of her out of his head. Ena's firm rebuff had greatly offended Armistead and he swore that he couldn't live without her love. Again, Ena gave him a straight reply. She told him that he would never be happy with her; she was too much in love with her husband ever to please another man. Telling Armistead he needed a quiet, loving and tender wife she pushed him in the direction of Palmerston Street. Only a day later he proposed to Minnie and she accepted him.

Walking to her wedding reception at the Eagle and Child, her husband by her side and her family and friends laughing and chattering behind her, Minnie cried. The tears were not of sadness over what she was giving up, or of joy for the occasion — they were tears of disbelief for as the wedding party passed the newlyweds' home Minnie saw for the first time Armistead's wedding present to her. There on the window sill, looking out at the passing crowd sat a small tabby kitten — its eyes wide with excitement. Minnie smiled happily up at her husband. Maybe things weren't going to be so bad after all.

Jack Todd worked as a local storeman. He left the bringing up of his three wayward children to his wife Vi.

Always behind the London fashions, Weatherfield was hit by the new jazz craze only after people down South had moved on to the Charleston. The newspapers shocked the staid Victorian parents with their illustrations of the latest dresses with square necks and short skirts. Ivy Makepiece nearly threw her young son Will out into the street after she found him gazing dreamily at a picture of the scantily clad dancer Josephine Baker. As far as Ivy and her associates were concerned these sort of women were immoral and were only there to tempt the poor susceptible men into wicked thoughts and deeds. Staunch Catholic Bernie from the market used to say prayers for Josephine Baker's soul every night.

The first dance hall opened up in Weatherfield in 1927, in the old Alhambra building which had once been home to the town's successful music hall. On its opening night the young couples from the area tried to impress the judges in various dancing contests. Alfred and Ena Sharples had practised their favourite dance for hours in their front parlour. That night they walked off with first prize for dancing the best Black Bottom. Lilian Foyle also won a first prize, for her polished performance of the Charleston. However, her husband Tommy was not her partner, she preferred to dance with her brother-in-law Jack Todd.

The Todds moved into Number 9 Coronation Street in 1926. The previous occupants, the Bucks, had moved to Newcastle after Ned Buck had died of pneumonia. Vi Todd was the eldest Makepiece child before her marriage to Jack in 1914. They lived with his mother Kelly at 16 Mawdsley Street for a while, but had moved to Corona-

Dressed in their fashionable finery, Ena and Alfred Sharples showed what they were made of when they Black Bottomed their way into winning a china dinner service at the Alhambra in 1922.

tion Street after her death, as Vi's mother Ivy was living alone at Number 11. The old lady refused to let the family move in with her but, appreciating their genuine concern for her welfare, persuaded the landlord to rent them the house next door. The Todd children, Jim, Sally and Dot were already well known in the street as petty thieves and truants. Their cousins, Alice and Harry Hewitt, were held in high regard by the family as they both regularly attended Bessie Street School, more through fear of their father's belt than any good intention to improve themselves.

Sid and Alice Hayes were proud to show off their second daughter, Esther, born in 1924.

Coronation Street, like all other Weatherfield streets, rang with the sound of children's voices during the Twenties. The population increased dramatically in the area, it was almost as though those who had survived the Great War were trying to fill the gaps left by those who had died. Alice Hayes gave birth to a little girl, Esther, in 1924 and two years later her son Tom was born. Tom's thanksgiving service at the Mission was ruined when the toddler, Esther, disappeared. The residents searched for her for four hours before she was found crying in the Mission basement where she had become trapped.

Billy Chad from Number 3 Coronation Street caused a scandal in 1925 by running off with his neighbour Susie Makepiece. His wife Flo was distraught at his disappearance and had to be sedated by a doctor. Her mother Gertie had a doorstep row, much to the delight of her neighbours, with her old enemy Ivy Makepiece. Those residents who could remember the glorious rows these women had partaken in were disappointed by this one. Exhausted by their hard lives, they both ended up weeping together at the way their families had never lived up to their expectations. Billy Chad returned in 1928 and was relieved to find Flo was still willing to have him back. She had always believed he would return and had continued to lay out a place for him on the table every meal time. Ivy never asked after Susie and Billy never told her that her daughter had now become a prostitute on the streets of London.

Despite the worries of many of the Weatherfield locals about having officials too close to hand, the completion of the Town Hall and surrounding park, which was finished in 1928, was greeted with much admiration. Tom Lingard, from Number 13, led a team of six gardeners to work on the Town Hall's grounds and was pleased when the results of their many hours of hard work were so well received by the local residents.

≋ THE DISAPPEARANCE OF TOM LINGARD ≋

'I get as much satisfaction from a well-presented border as I do from a pint of mild.'

Number 14 Rosamund Street was to be turned into a shop. The house had been home to Carrie Lingard since her husband died in 1898. Recently her son Tom and his wife Nellie had lodged with her, and their daughter Ada had been born in the back bedroom in 1913. Now, six years and a world war further on, Carrie was dead and the Lingards had been served notice to quit the premises. They were given just two weeks notice to vacate their home.

Nellie Lingard was 25 years old. At the age of 13, as Nellie Preston, she had been the youngest weaver in Hardcastle's weaving shed. Her swift and nimble fingers had been renowned at the mill, but they were now suffering the effects of premature arthritis, and she was still only in her twenties. Nellie had continued to work for Hardcastle, while many of her workmates had left to earn more money working in the munitions factories. Nellie felt a strong loyalty to Hardcastle who had employed her family for years. Now, to repay her allegiance, Hardcastle agreed to rent the family Number 13 Coronation Street, now vacant after the Piggotts' departure.

Tom Lingard was well known to the residents of Coronation Street. The Rovers had been his local since he was old enough to drink, and for a man of slight build, he still managed to put away more than his fair share of best bitter. He was a gardener by trade, a strange profession for a Weatherfield man as the only green in the town appeared to be the grass growing in the gutters. Surprisingly enough Tom was never short of work. He was employed by the Corporation to tend to the grass verges along the canal and in the early Twenties was drafted onto a job that was to help change the face of Weatherfield.

Since the Weatherfield Pit Disaster in 1906, the coal pit and slag heaps between Alexandra Terrace and Edward Street had remained untouched. Years of scavenging in the heaps had left the whole area void of coal, but the black empty buildings and mounds of slag were a permanent reminder of the town's premier business and the tragedy that had closed it down. Somewhere under the streets between Edward Street and Viaduct Street lay the bodies of nearly four hundred men. For their families left on the surface, the pit served as a holy shrine and a ghostly reminder of their grief.

Part of the colliery land had been converted into a cemetery to house the overspill from St Mary's graveyard which was full by 1910. The cemetery housed a monument erected in memory of the lost miners. Now, ten years later, the Council decided to replan the whole site. The residents of Weatherfield were relieved at the plans to turn the pit face into a park, but were not so keen at the prospect of a Town Hall. They were used to travelling into Manchester if they needed to seek official help and the semi-literate inhabitants found the prospect of their Council peers being so close quite frightening.

Tom Lingard was employed as one of the senior gardeners to landscape the grounds around the new Town Hall building. A landscape gardener from Manchester trained Tom and his six workmates for a week, after which they were left to cope on their own. Tom, returning home to

Tom Lingard had served in the Red Cross during the war. He was a peace-loving man and enjoyed his time nurturing flowers.

Nellie Lingard adored her husband Tom and was confused by his inexplicable disappearance in 1929.

Coronation Street each night, told his pals at the Rovers of the huge sums of money the Council were spending on the project. Not one of the residents complained that the money could be put to better use in housing or education; they were all impressed by the beauty that was being created under their very noses.

The Town Hall was completed in 1928. It was an impressive building with a sweeping drive and fir trees all around it. Tom himself had planted each of the trees and had designed the borders that surrounded the bandstand in the park. The whole site looked splendid, at least as far as Tom was concerned. He was very proud to be present at the grand opening of the Town Hall on 22 December 1928.

The Lingards had a very happy Christmas that year. Tom was told his next job would be to landscape the hillside area at the top of town towards Oakhill where large semi-detached houses were to be developed. As he set off for work on the morning of 3 January 1929, he did so with a spring in his step. The New Year looked promising for the family, even though Nellie had had lost all feeling in her right hand and had to give up work. She kissed Tom as he left the house, as usual, and set about her daily chores. When Tom did not return for his tea she became concerned: he was a punctual man and was very strict about eating his meals on time. Tom still did not return that evening. By morning Nellie was frantic, but did not know what to do or whom to turn to for help. When Tom's workmate called at the house asking after Tom as he had not been at work the previous day, Nellie excused Tom, explaining he was ill in bed with a bad cold.

Days turned into a week and the strain started to show in the Lingard house. Ada and Mary, following their mother's lead, had covered up for their father's absence. Now they realized they couldn't continue to do so. Where was Tom Lingard? The police were brought in by George Diggins, landlord of the Rovers. They too were baffled by the disappearance of this quiet family man. At the suggestion that Tom might have run off with another woman Nellie broke down. She wondered if that was right, could she have driven Tom away?

Tom's body was found floating under Blackpool Central Pier on the morning of 30 January. There was no mark on him and no indication as to how he had died. Was it suicide? Had he been drunk? What was he doing in Blackpool? These questions were never to be answered and the mystery remains to this day. With the family's source of income removed, Nellie was forced to give up the house in Coronation Street and throw herself at the mercy of the Corporation. In February the family were forced to leave the house with just a suitcase to enter Council care.

The reading room at the Library was always full each morning as the national and local papers were avidly scanned for jobs by those out of work. It was these newspapers that first carried to Weatherfield the news that the American stock market had crashed. Suddenly all talk was about the possible repercussions in Britiain. The talk was now of recession and high unemployment. The people of Weatherfield knew little about life in America; all they knew was what they gleaned from the cinema screen. Nothing, they said to themselves, could be as bad as the recession they had come through in the last years after World War I, nothing could be as bad as that surely.

Ex-prize-fighter and retired police sergeant George Diggins took over the management of the Rover's Return Inn in 1919.

CHAPTER 5

1930-1939: THE GLOOM OF THE DEPRESSION

PURE SILK STOCKINGS *free* to smokers of

TURF
QUALITY CIGARETTES

Silk stocking on offer with every packet of 'gaspers'. Few in Weatherfield in 1934 could afford even the sixpence to start collecting the coupons. Even fewer could afford silk stocking by any other means.

THE NEWS RACED through Coronation Street, Mawdsley Street and Victoria Street like wild fire. It had been expected, but no one had really been prepared for the closure of Hardcastle's Cotton Mill. Half of the houses situated on these streets contained families that worked at the mill and all of the houses had been built around that empire. For nearly 50 years Hardcastle had been *the* name in Weatherfield. The family owned a warehouse, two mill sites, the factory school, a tailoring factory and, including Mabel Hardcastle's inheritance, the very land, houses and shops between Rosamund Street and Viaduct Street.

Mabel Hardcastle had been widowed in 1926. Her stepson Matthew had taken over the running of the family firm but he was not the great businessman his father had been. The company suffered from market forces like many other Weatherfield businesses; the Great War had resulted in the loss of manufacturing markets to cheaper industrial rivals overseas and the demand for British goods had been reduced. Cotton exports were reduced by half between 1929 and 1931, the Government had difficulties in handling labour relations, and the pound was over-valued. Hardcastle's, like many other English firms, was forced to shut down production. The bottom had fallen out of their market.

For the people of Coronation Street, Hardcastle's closure in 1931 meant unemployment on a large scale with little hope of finding jobs anywhere else; by 1931 a third of Weatherfield was looking for jobs. The workers at Hardcastle's had thought they were going to be spared the dole queues and means tests, but they were mistaken.

Even though times were hard, people moved from other areas to seek work in Weatherfield, hearing that the situation there was better than the hardships they were suffering at home. Other families moved because of changed circumstances — the Beaumonts were one of them.

⚞ ANNE BEAUMONT RISES AGAIN ⚟

'One does get rather tired of this dreary landscape. This desert of bricks and cobbled streets. Blackened chimneys piercing the sultry sky like jagged teeth.'

Twenty-one-year-old Anne Beaumont had mixed emotions about leaving her home town of Clitheroe. Her family was one of the oldest in that Lancashire town and the name still commanded some respect. Unfortunately, the last thirty years had not been kind to the Clitheroe Beaumonts; Grandpapa had invested the family fortune unwisely, and on his death, his eldest son Edward had discovered numerous debts and unpaid bills.

Edward's small family, his wife Florence and daughter Anne, were left to shoulder the burden of the old man's debts as his brothers and sisters hastily left Clitheroe not wanting to part with any of *their* money. The year was 1927 and the only employment open to the family was in the cotton industry. Edward managed to obtain a post as senior clerk in a mill office. Florence was saved the horrors of the factory floor, but Anne was deemed young and strong enough to cope with the work and was placed in a weaving shed, working alongside the sort of person her mother had always advised her not to talk to in the street. Anne learned to adopt a dignified aloofness in her manner and refused to be drawn into any arguments or fights with the women who jeered at her 'posh' accent and mannerisms. They were, she told herself firmly, quite beneath her contempt.

The Beaumonts came to England with William the Conqueror, and Anne often praised the Lord that they had. Unlike the Anglo-Saxons she found herself living amongst, her ancestry left her with a sophisticated, continental view on life and the arts.

For three years Anne struggled on working at the mill. She mastered the machinery very quickly and the work she produced was of a fine standard. Each evening she would read by the light of the fire to her mother whilst her father kept a close eye on the family accounts. Each night Edward promised Anne that they would rise again as a family of means, and each night Anne would pray that that day would soon come.

The day of fortune finally came on 7 April 1930. Florence's unmarried aunt, Isabella Scattergood, died and in her will left her successful ice cream factory to her niece. The factory was situated in Weatherfield and had grown since the turn of the century from a back-room ice cream shop, where the ice cream was produced by hand in a small barrel, into a thriving factory, employing thirty people. The Beaumonts left Clitheroe and moved across country to Weatherfield where they found the locals to be as friendly as at home.

Anne was thrilled with the factory — it was such an improvement. No more looms, no more hooters, no more nattering dirty women, no more twelve-hour days. Instead she helped her father run the whiter-than-white factory where all the staff wore crisp aprons and hats over their hair. The air smelt of a mixture of carbolic and vanilla essence and the tiled floor shone from the fervent scrubbing of four cleaners.

Anne helped her father at the factory every morning. After her lunch she caught a tram from the factory on Irlam Road to the Weatherfield

Lyceum on Upper Edward Street, just opposite the new Town Hall. There she took singing lessons, which were her father's treat and reward for her having endured the three years' sentence at the loom. Here, at the Lyceum, people were paid to pamper her, humour her opinion of herself and instruct her skilfully in the art of singing and of public speaking. The Lyceum was built on the old site of St Agnes' church and the amateur operatic society, which met there twice a week, named themselves after the church. Anne eagerly joined the group, warning group leader Edgar Nuttall that she would not stay in the chorus for long. She was given her first lead in 1932 in *Mayfair Melody*. After her opening night, she walked home with her mother's sable fur over her shoulders. She hardly noticed stepping over the line of men asleep on the pavement, waiting for the Labour Exchange to open in the morning.

With the family's fortunes improving, Anne turned her thoughts to finding a suitable man to marry. Suitable for Anne meant a good family name, a large income, a love of the arts and the ability to wear a uniform well — although she would settle for a dress suit if necessary. Armed with her list of requirements, Anne started to assess prospective bridegrooms. Arthur Moxon rated quite highly on her list. His mother was a widow of independent means, and Arthur was an only child. He swore he'd die for her, but unfortunately he did, literally, when he was knocked down and killed by a tram whilst walking on his hands trying to impress her.

Lay preacher, Lionel Blinnie, proposed marriage to Anne on their third evening together, without even having taken her home to meet his parents. Anne knew her father would not approve of Lionel as he didn't trust men who didn't drink, so she flatly turned him down. She later heard he'd been sent to Africa as a missionary and felt that was perhaps the best place for him. Another suitor, Edward Etherington, was so desperate to marry Anne that he secured a job for her as a stewardess on board the cruise ship where he served as a petty officer. Anne was very touched that he wanted them to be together as much as possible, and decided to accept the offer. After all, he did look so dashing in his uniform, just like Lionel Barrymore. Unfortunately, she had to put a stop to her plans when her mother reminded her she was seasick even travelling on the Isle of Man ferry.

Both Edward and Florence approved when Anne started to court her cousin, Edwin Beaumont. Edwin worked in Manchester in a city bank and even Anne had to admit he did meet all her special requirements. Moreover, he was a fun and amusing person to be with. He insisted on calling her Annie and she decided the name suited her more than just plain Anne. Taking up a dare from Edwin, Annie agreed to enter the local Pageant of the Ages. Edwin's condition was that he would choose the character that she was to play.

On the morning of the pageant, Annie was pleased to see that Edwin had gathered all the family members together to watch the procession go down Rosamund Street. She was puzzled however to note that Edwin was nowhere to be seen. Arriving at the Co-op hall for her costume, she was finally informed by the organizer what her character was to be. She was

Edwin Beaumont was a prankster and a wit. Unfortunately his wit failed him when he was transported to Australia for embezzlement.

dumbstruck as he handed her just a body stocking and a blonde wig. She hunted for Edwin, but of course he was nowhere to be found. The knowledge that all her family were waiting caused her to panic. And then it all came back to her. She remembered the pitiful sight of her father crying over the extent of Grandpapa's debts. How all their family had deserted them in their hour of need. How only now, when they were once more respectable, that the Beaumonts had started to visit again. She remembered the jeering of the weavers, the cuts on her fingers as she operated the looms, and the way her father had always promised things would improve.

She was a Beaumont. She had risen back up from the depths of despair. And she would show her so-called relations that a true Beaumont never dodged a responsibility and was able to take anything life threw at her. As the crowds cheered and waved their flags, Annie sat bolt upright on the milkman's horse. As Lady Godiva passed the waiting Beaumont clan, she smiled and waved majestically and had the smug satisfaction of seeing her Aunt Maud faint and fall into the gutter.

⬅ GENTLEMAN JACK WALKER ➡

'I learned at an early age to trust folk. It's the best way. If you trust someone you always find they won't abuse that trust. It's one of the best things about human nature.'

The Nag's Head public house stood on the corner of Canal Street and Upper Edward Street. Its customers were mainly older men, who had grown used to visiting their local when they worked on the canal barges in the nineteenth century. The pub was run by Tom Pickles with the help of his daughter Cissy and her husband Arthur Walker. Cissy and Arthur had married in 1932 and were relieved to be able to work in the pub; a third of the men in Weatherfield were unemployed and the numbers walking the streets in search of work was increasing daily.

Built on the highest point of Canal Street, the pub's bedroom windows had a fine view over the roof tops of Weatherfield and the Walkers could actually see above some of the polluting smoke that affected all the town's residents. The view did have its drawbacks. From the back windows, overlooking the canal, you could see the bodies of the suicide victims, who had given up on life, as they bobbed in the water. In 1933 alone Arthur Walker helped pull 27 bodies from the canal. It was the sight of Arthur trying to resuscitate one such unfortunate which greeted Jack Walker when he arrived in Weatherfield for the first time, in the winter of 1933.

Back home in Accrington, Jack had not worked for 16 months. His brother Arthur had told him that the unemployment rate was slightly lower in Weatherfield, so Jack arrived with a suitcase and moved into the tiny box room at the Nag's Head on the understanding he would work four evenings a week behind the bar to earn his keep. However, it was agreed

John ('Jack') Walker left his native Accrington, where his father Amos worked as a veterinary surgeon, to look for work in Weatherfield in 1933.

that he wouldn't be paid for these sessions and would have to find work to fill his days and to give him an income.

Jack could not believe his luck when on his second day of looking for employment he was offered a job. He thought, perhaps, he should refuse it as he felt as if he were depriving a local person of the job. However, his common sense told him not to be so stupid and to take the opportunity while he could. The job was at Possitt's dye works on Nightingale Row, alongside the canal. Jack noted with alarm that the company regularly discarded waste dye into the canal. Jack's new job was to push the carts of wool delivered from Chasen's Mill into the dye rooms.

It was while he was pushing a cart along the canal to the work's entrance that he saw a young woman standing on the pack-horse bridge on Clarence Street. The bridge was tall and the woman stood staring bleakly into the murky waters below. The dye had stained the water purple giving it the appearance of ink. Jack could clearly see the young woman's attractive face reflected in the water. It suddenly occurred to Jack what the woman was doing, standing there, on that high bridge, gazing into the water below. Jack started to run towards her, determined that this was one body he wasn't going to help Arthur fish out from the canal.

As the woman turned to see who it was that was shouting at her, Jack tripped on a cobble and smashed to the ground before her. She bent over him and helped him up. Their eyes met and she smiled at him. Jack grabbed hold of her arm and told her that she must stop what she was doing. The woman was alarmed by the severity of his tone and fearing he might attack her she called for help. He let her arm go and tried to quieten her down. One of his workmates arrived to see what was going on and Jack explained that he was stopping this woman from killing herself.

At this point Annie Beaumont stopped shouting for the police. The man wasn't attacking her, he had been trying to save her. How sweet, how gallant. She explained that nothing was wrong, she had merely stopped on the bridge to look at the unusual coloured water. They introduced themselves and Jack felt unusually shy in her presence. They lingered for a while on the bridge, but he suddenly realized he was supposed to be working and should get back to his cart. Annie noted where he worked and remarked that she used the bridge every day; she worked on Irlam Road, in a factory. He commented that he hoped they'd meet again. She didn't reply, but just smiled coyly.

As he watched Annie walk off across the neighbouring croft, Jack smiled and told himself that one day he would marry that bonny lass with the posh accent.

Albert Tatlock quietly congratulated himself on his own good fortune; he had been employed at the cotton mill from a young lad until 1929 when he had taken a better paid job at the local print works. His wife Bessie had stayed on in the weaving shed, but luckily they could just manage on his earnings. The Hewitts at Number 7 were not so fortunate; both parents had been employed at the mill and their children, Alice and Harry, were serving apprenticeships at Hardcastle's factory school. Whilst teacher Ada Hayes assured them their education would continue, their half-days earning money at the mill would, of course, now stop.

The Depression hit Weatherfield very hard. The quality of life had

Bank teller George Hardman married May Mason in 1930. Unlike the other families in the street, the Hardmans lived in their front parlour.

been improving year by year since the war. Regular employment had been found for most of the ex-soldiers and for the women who wanted to work. The residents enjoyed a higher standard of living than ever before and leisure activities were beginning to flourish. Now, faced with enforced leisure, the Weatherfield people found themselves having to think about surviving on a pittance. The average family, with both parents out of work and three children to feed, received in benefit from the state a maximum of 29 shillings and three pence. Each family with a man who had been unemployed for more than six months had to undergo a means test in which any other source of household income was taken account of and deducted from the family's benefits.

The Mission of Glad Tidings opened its doors each Sunday to a

33-year-old Albert Tatlock lost his job at the local print works in the early 1930s.

declining number of chapel-goers. It was not that people had given up on God; they were just too embarrassed to attend as they could not afford to put any money in the offering box. After the box had been broken into twice by men desperate for money, the committee agreed to remove it to save anyone any further embarrassment.

Twenty-year-old Molly Hewitt missed the Depression completely in Weatherfield by leaving to start a new life for herself in America. She married Artie Longswaite, a native of Salford who had made his fortune mining in Canada. Molly's fairy-tale wedding brought some much needed happiness into the gloom of Weatherfield and although the excitement died with the Longswaites' departure, the memory of the happy occasion lived in the neighbours' minds for months afterwards. Shortly after Molly's wedding, in 1930, a new family moved into Coronation Street's tragedy house — Number 13. George Hardman and his bride May were worried by the neighbours' tales of woe about the former inhabitants — the Harrisons' deaths, Emma Piggott's insanity and Tom Lingard's mystery disappearance. As it turned out, the Hardmans were one of the few Weatherfield families to come through the 1930s unscathed. George managed to keep his secure job as a bank clerk whilst May annoyed her hard-pressed neighbours by offering them advice on close budgeting and how to make household economies. The Longhurst family of Mawdsley Street were not so lucky, as unemployment steadily rose Martha's husband Percy, who was a weaver, was soon to become another one of its victims.

Molly Hewitt provided the area with a fairy tale romance and wedding when she was whisked away to an affluent life in America.

≋ MARTHA'S LOST WEEKEND ≋

'What am I? A drudge in a town full of drudges?'

The idea had sounded fun at the time — to wear a wedding dress again, to hold a bouquet again, to smile at a photographer. She had always wanted a wedding photograph, always regretted that they had not been able to afford one in 1919. But now, eleven years later, as she stood outside the local chapel with Percy once again on her arm she felt cheated. The exciting glow and anticipation she had felt at twenty had long since faded. The dress did not fit properly now and she had a headache.

Martha Longhurst was a sad woman. The joy she had experienced as a young bride had been replaced by bitterness at all the injustices in life. She had been brought up in a joyful home and had grown to expect the same from her own house on Mawdsley Street, but she had been disappointed. The last ten years had seen both her mother and invalided sister die, she had miscarried two babies and seen her only son drown in Mosley's Flash. Little Lily was all that was left to her. Her womb had been damaged after the last miscarriage and the doctor had warned her not to try for

Percy and Martha Longhurst married twice — once for real in 1919 and then again eleven years later, for photographs.

another child. Fearing his words, from that moment on Martha decided she was taking no chances and refused to let Percy touch her.

The photograph looked out of place on the bare kitchen mantle. With Percy out of work, along with nearly half the local men, the Longhursts tasted real poverty for the first time. It was true that they had suffered hard times before, but things had never been this desperate. Martha managed to hang onto her charring job at the Town Hall, but the family couldn't survive on her wages alone.

Martha understood how demoralized Percy felt. He was still young and she cared for him deeply. His pride was broken when he 'celebrated' his first year of unemployment. His feet were weary from trailing the streets every day searching for work. His body always felt cold from lack of warm clothing and good food. He accused Martha of denying him any physical comfort at home and told her he no longer loved her. She knew he didn't really mean it — the thing that upset him the most was that she had taken over as breadwinner.

Percy Longhurst walked out on his family in the summer of 1934. He had found employment in late 1932 as a storeman in a local warehouse, and during that time, his faith in himself restored, he had embarked on an affair with the barmaid from the Kings Arms. Martha had known all about it. She had not blamed him; how could she? After all she wasn't doing her duty to him as

Martha Longhurst enjoyed every minute of her special weekend away in Blackpool. She would keep the memory of her few days of freedom as a treasured secret all her life.

a wife and it was natural that he looked elsewhere. She was surprised and very hurt though when he had actually decided to run off with the woman.

It was a hot summer. Too hot to be stuck in Mawdsley Street. There was no sign of Percy returning just yet, although Martha was certain he would come home soon. Suddenly she felt it was time *she* had a break — perhaps Percy had the right idea. She told Minnie Caldwell that she was borrowing the money to visit an aunt in Leeds.

She lied; in fact the train she caught travelled in the opposite direction. With Lily left in the care of Ena Sharples, Martha planned to enjoy herself for a few days all by herself in Blackpool.

She paddled and ran along the beach. She ate whelks straight out of a paper cup and laughed at her own mischief. She was acting totally out of character and loved every minute of it. No one knew her; no one recognized her as the shabby woman who hated blacking her grate. She was an individual again — she was happy and free. Percy and Lil were never out of her mind and Weatherfield was always just round the corner. She knew that but didn't care. For the first time in her life Martha wanted to live just for the moment. She understood now why Percy had run off, why he had to get away. Why shouldn't he? Why should anyone have to spend each and every day in that dark, depressing, smoke-filled town. Martha pushed thoughts of Weatherfield to the back of her mind. This weekend was hers and she was going to enjoy it, every minute of it.

The workers at Hardcastle's factory lost their jobs in September 1931, just in time to participate in the organized demonstrations in Weatherfield and Salford. Throughout the autumn, the unemployed marched on the labour exchanges and town halls in protest against the cuts in state benefit. These unemployed men had served their country in the the Great War, they had been promised good homes, well-paid jobs and even a cow each! They had come back to the same slum houses; they did not really mind not having a cow, but had they really risked their lives for a country which left them without employment? Shouting 'Remember 1914' the crowds marched on Weatherfield Town Hall. Little children ran barefoot amongst the demonstrators whilst someone at the head of the crowd waved an impressive red flag.

Mounted police were drafted in to break up the demonstration, and with their batons at the ready they used their horses to drive back angry protesters. Nine of the ringleaders were arrested and more demonstrations were held in protest at this insult. If the people of Weatherfield had no jobs, they decided to use their time to protest. As Christmas 1931 approached, the sight of police guarding public buildings and shops became commonplace.

The summer of 1932 brought a ray of hope to the inhabitants of the streets surrounding Hardcastle's Mill. Black Jack Elliston, a local councillor well known for his top hat and jovial smile, opened a factory in the empty mill and started to make raincoats for the home market. He advertised for machinists and storemen and was shocked to find on the morning of the interviews a queue of hopeful people which stretched from the factory door down Victoria Street and into Lower Edward Street. Elliston had only forty jobs on offer and he mentally filled these posts after seeing two hundred applicants. However, he insisted on interviewing all the other applicants, six hundred in all, to let them feel that at least for one day they had done something useful and stood a chance of getting a job. Mary Hewitt was the only applicant from Coronation Street to be employed by Elliston. The money she received from her job saved her family from the workhouse.

In February 1935, Albert Tatlock lost his job at the print works and signed on the dole for the first time. The same day he read in one of the newspapers in the library reading room that Rochdale singer Gracie Fields had signed a film contract worth £150,000. It just wasn't real. Three months later, the residents of Coronation Street attempted to forget their troubles for a day and brought out their tables and chairs for a street party in honour of King George V's Silver Jubilee. Albert spent the day looking after his two-year-old daughter

Beattie as Bessie queued to try to get a job on the other side of town. The actual interviews were to be the next day but applicants were settling themselves down for the night. All families were affected and Alfred Sharples began to fear for his job — nothing seem to be secure any more.

⤳ ENA SHARPLES — THE SURVIVOR ⤶

'I've walked barefoot before. I've scavenged in the gutter with the other bairns in our street. I've seen me mother weep over an empty pot. But I've never begged and as the Lord Almighty is my witness, I never shall!'

Alfred Sharples lost his job in 1935. At the time, his wife Ena was not working; she had left Hardcastle's Mill just before her first child Vera was

Ena Sharples and husband Alfred posed in their back yard for each other in front of a borrowed camera. The smiles on their faces would soon disappear as Alfred lost his job and the Depression left its mark on their lives.

born in 1921. Now, with two daughters and only a gravestone to mark the birth of her only son, taken from her after just six days, Ena was meant to run the home at 65 Inkerman Street, cook and clothe the family on her husband's dole money of just twenty-nine shillings and three pence a week. It was going to be hard, but she forced herself to believe Alfred when he told her he was a good worker and, unlike many of the unemployed, he was willing and able to work. They would, he assured her, treat this brief period of rest as a holiday.

The short respite was not to be and Alfred was forced to undergo a means test in 1936. He had by then been out of work for six months. In desperation, Ena had taken in washing to supplement their income. Vera had the start of tuberculosis and Madge had left school and was sent out early each morning to Plank Lane market to follow the fruit barrow as it was set up, in the hope she could catch any fallen fruit. Alfred's holiday attitude had turned into a feeling of anxiety, as he watched Ena growing thinner as she neglected her own welfare for the sake of the children. Her piano, which she'd inherited from her grandmother, was sold so they could qualify for a means test. Their dole was raised to thirty-six shillings.

Alfred developed a bad cough in December 1936. His anxiety about finding work had now turned into depression. Madge, even at her tender age, had emigrated to Canada in search of possible work. Vera was recovering from the worst of her illness, but was unable to work. Ena took a job playing the pit piano at the Electric Picture Palace. The pay was minimal but, taking Vera with her, at least they managed to keep warm each evening. Her husband Alfred joined a protest march against the high unemployment, demanding work with his neighbours and friends.

Despite all Ena's efforts, Alfred died on 19 March 1937. The death certificate detailed the cause of death as pneumonia. Ena said it was chronic depression brought on by being forced out of work and forgotten by the well-off bosses and managers who still drove around the streets in their motor cars, while she and her own starved in basic houses and many had to resort to begging for food.

Mary Diggins was glad to leave the Rovers Return after 19 years' service behind the bar. The Diggins retired to the coast in 1938.

※

Slowly life began to improve in Weatherfield again. New businesses started up and replaced the traditional manufacturing export market. The Council allocated funds for new housing. Semi-detached properties were built for private sale towards the north of town, near Oakhill. Chasen's Mill and Marshall's Cotton Mill were demolished and council housing estates were built on the sites. These houses even had gardens.

New families started to move into Coronation Street. At the Rovers Return, landlord George Diggins (who had served as a Special Constable during the unrest of 1931) decided to retire to

Granny Chad moved into Number 3 Coronation Street with her son Billy and his wife Flo (right) in 1934. After her death in 1936 the Chads emigrated to America.

Southport and the pub was sold back to the brewery. Newton, Ridley, Oakes and Company replaced the Diggins with the Walker family. Jack Walker had written to the brewery in hope of getting employment and had acquired bar experience working at the Nag's Head by the canal. His wife Annie was to help him at the Rovers when she was not looking after her baby son, Billy.

The Chads left the street in 1938. They had survived the Depression on Flo's barmaid's wages at the Rovers and food stolen from shops by Billy. Molly Longswaite called on the couple when she was back in the country for a visit. She was appalled by their standard of living and immediately booked them a passage to America. Their house was rented out to GPO sorter Frank Barlow and his wife Ida.

⚐ STEADY, DEPENDABLE FRANK BARLOW ⚐

'I'm not a great one for words, nor actions. I know I'm not going to make a great splash in life. The trouble with lots o' folk is they expect too much out o' life.'

The church bells rang out loud and clear on Sunday 1 May 1938. It was a beautiful spring day and the congregation at St Mary's Parish Church commented that summer had indeed arrived early — especially for the

Frank Barlow joined the Navy aged 16. His hopes for a long naval career were dashed when his mother became mentally ill and he felt he had to return.

young couple who had just said their wedding vows. As the bridesmaids, their wide-brimmed hats shading their eyes from the direct sunlight, posed for photographs with the bride and groom, Nancy Leathers and Edna Barlow chatted excitedly about the plans their children had for the future.

Frank Barlow felt very uncomfortable in his wedding suit, his collar felt too tight and the church had been unbearably hot. The humbug he had been sucking to quell his nervousness had left his throat parched, and his new shoes were pinching his toes. He was being told to smile for the photographer so he did, briefly. Beside him his wife of twenty minutes chatted to her sisters about how she thought she was going to trip on her hem, say the wrong words and, of course, how happy she now felt.

Frank supposed he also was happy. He certainly felt pleased to be married to Ida and he was looking forward to the spread his mother had laid on. All morning the smell of ham boiled with onions had kept his mind off the forthcoming ceremony. Next to his favourite food, tripe and onions, Frank enjoyed a nice cut of ham. And then there would be the moment when they'd be alone for the first time in what had been his parents' room. He pushed the thought to the back of his mind. Far better to think about that tasty ham and onions.

At 16 he looked 14 and had joined the Navy to see something of the world. He had always been a quiet, thoughtful chap and enjoyed being in the company of men. Women scared him, they always had done. At school he had seldom acknowledged the presence of his sister Marj or any of her girlfriends. He did not join in with the boys who had teased the girls, dabbing their pony tails into ink wells and worse. He had always kept a respectable distance from them and hoped they would do the same from him.

The two years that Frank had spent in the Navy had taught him to rely even more on men. Women became something to be bragged about, at least a certain sort of woman was. Not that Frank had anything to brag about, he just listened along with the others to the tales of conquest. Half embarrassed, half intrigued, he always kept women at a distance and they became even more of a mystery to him.

Sidney Barlow died when his son Frank was eighteen. His widow Edna was unable to cope with just her daughter Marjorie for company and suffered a nervous breakdown. She became obsessed with cleanliness and took to polishing, sweeping and cleaning every inch of her home at 6 Mawdsley Street. When at one point Marjorie accidentally spilt a jug of peas, scattering them all over the freshly swept kitchen floor, Edna was aghast. She flew at the girl, shouting and hitting her about the head. Marjorie ran screaming into the street with her mother following her. The neighbours came to Marj's aid, and two men had to restrain Edna who continued to scream obscenities at her daughter. A policeman was sent for and Edna was taken down to the Tile Street police station.

Upon hearing the news that his mother was mentally ill, Frank was faced with a big decision. His training with the Navy had come to an end and he was being asked to sign up for further service. He enjoyed working on ships and had made some good pals, but his sense of family loyalty finally won him over and he decided to leave the Navy. Edna was being treated in a psychiatric hospital and Marjorie was occupied working at Earnshaw's Mill. She was a trained weaver and when Hardcastle's Mill closed down she had managed to obtain a job at Earnshaw's, down by the docks. Frank found there was little for him to do at home and began to regret his decision to try and help out. The only employment open to him was at the GPO where his father had worked. Frank had served six months as a telegram boy upon leaving school and was not keen to return to the job. However, he did need money to help run the house and decided to take the job of postman until a better position came up.

To the residents of Mawdsley Street, Gladys Marshall was a scarlet woman and possibly a murderess. To Frank Barlow she was a caring confidante.

Elsie Castleway took Coronation Street by storm: with her peroxide hair and painted red lips, she took control of Tommy Foyle's life and made herself at home at the corner shop.

Edna Barlow was allowed home after three months of treatment. She was a very different person: she had become subdued and fearful of what the neighbours thought of her. Frank tried his best to cheer her up, but found it very hard work. He knew he could never replace his father in her life. It was ironic that after all Frank's attempts to bring his mother back to her old self, he managed to do just that one day, quite accidentally. Gossip soon reached Edna's ears that her son had been seen walking out with Gladys Marshall from the tobacconist on the corner. Gladys was regarded with some suspicion by the local women. She was nearly thirty, a native of Birmingham and had married tobacconist Ted Marshall only a month before he had died, complaining of stomach pains. To Martha Longhurst at Number 17 and the rest of Mawdsley Street, the woman was obviously a murderess and no amount of doctors' explanations would convince them that the truth was otherwise.

Although she didn't go along with Martha's theories, Edna did not like the idea of Frank seeing the woman. Without listening to Frank's explanation of why he had been walking with Gladys (in truth he had been helping her home after she had twisted her ankle on a loose cobble), Edna launched in to a verbal attack. She forbade her son to see Gladys again saying that she was nearly 10 years his senior, a widow, an outsider, and what was more she wore far too much make-up. Frank was astounded by this outburst, but relieved to see that his mother was back to her former self. He humbly begged her forgiveness and promised not to entertain wicked thoughts about Mrs Marshall. He did not tell his mother that he had, for a brief period, felt himself attracted to Gladys, that she had guessed and had advised him to wait for 'the right girl' to come along.

Strangely enough the right girl came along that very evening of Edna's outburst. As Edna was setting the table for tea, Marjorie returned from the mill bringing with her a fellow worker. After establishing there was enough food for four, Marj introduced the family to her friend, the quiet Ida Leathers. As Frank stood by the fire sucking his pipe, he listened to the two girls chatting. At one point he caught Ida's eye and she gave him a shy smile; suddenly life did not seem so bad and Frank felt at peace with himself.

The Mission of Glad Tidings lost its loyal caretaker of 35 years when Gladys Arkwright died. She suffered an undignified end, in the gutter outside the Rovers Return where Billy Chad had pushed her, when she had reprimanded him for not attending chapel. Everyone agreed that Gladys had banged her head on the cobbles accidentally, but Ena Sharples, who took over from her old friend as caretaker, haunted Billy until he emigrated. The Sharples, Ena and her 18-year-old daughter Vera, moved into the Mission Vestry on the sad afternoon they buried Alfred Sharples in 1937.

Number 11 Coronation Street also fell vacant; 75-year-old Ivy Makepiece, the warring battle-axe, had finally died in her sleep. Her daughter, Vi Todd from Number 9, had no money to pay for a decent funeral, so the old lady was buried by the parish in a pauper's grave.

The Tatlocks at Number 1 celebrated in March 1937 when Albert became a clerk at the Town Hall in the housing department. As he worked in local government, his neighbours sought his opinion when talk of another war reached them. No one really wanted to believe that another conflict was possible; the shock of the abdication of Edward VIII and the coronation of George VI had held everyone's attention. However, with Hitler dominating Europe, the Bessie Street School held gas-mask drills and staged mock evacuations. The children thought it all great fun, but their parents and grandparents found the demonstration disturbing. The horrors of the Great War were still fresh in many people's minds. Were they really to go through it all again?

Horlock's, 'the daintiest shop in town', was owned by spinster Daisy Horlock who set up shop in 1930. She ran the shop in Rosamund Street single-handed, and specialized in low priced goods in keeping with the poverty of the area. The maternity dress in the advertisement was made to measure for 25 shillings.

CHAPTER 6

1939-1945: 'KEEP THE HOME FIRES BURNING'

As Alice Hewitt married Sam Burgess in September 1939, she was aware that most of the congregation's minds were on the planned speech by the Prime Minister Neville Chamberlain.

THE ONLY REGRET that Alice Hewitt had about marrying in chapel instead of church was that she couldn't have the bells rung. She need not have been disappointed, for in the event, the church bells of Weatherfield rang out loudly on Alice's wedding day, Sunday 3 September 1939.

The residents of Coronation Street heard the Prime Minister's declaration of war as they settled down for the wedding breakfast in the Select at the Rovers Return Inn. Jack Walker's wireless was set on the stage, next to the wedding cake and at 11am, exactly one hour after Alice and Sam Burgess had exchanged their vows, the expected news was announced. Alice refused to let the news of war spoil her day and insisted that the dancing start straight away. In the month that followed, the people of Weatherfield were bombarded with Government information leaflets, regulations and petty officialdom. They were instructed to paint the corners of their windows black, to stop any light escaping which would aid enemy bombers. Annie Walker refused to paint her smart windows and then suffered the indignation of being fined. Ena Sharples and Albert Tatlock elected themselves to be wardens for Coronation Street and their positions were made official by the arrival of their ARP helmets. Stirrup-pumps were delivered to all houses with detailed instructions on how to put out incendiary bombs and brick shelters were erected over the town.

War brought many changes to the street and it was in the midst of them that a new family — the Tanners — moved in.

≪ ELSIE MAKES HER MARK ≫

'They've got an old saying round 'ere — "there's no smoke without fire". It were invented around 'ere and it's wrecked a lot of inocent lives.'

World War Two had progressed into its second month when the new tenants of Number 11 Coronation Street moved in. The neighbours had heard of Arnold Tanner and his child bride through the local grapevine before their arrival. Arnold, a well-built local lad had 'leant' rather heavily on an elderly widow to vacate her house on Wright Street. Arnold had been paid for his trouble by landlord Wormold but had shrewdly refused the money and instead he'd asked for the tenancy of the vacant Number 11 for himself and his wife.

Elsie Tanner, née Grimshaw, was seven months pregnant when she demanded that Arnold should carry her over the threshold. Although only 16, Elsie gave the appearance of being in her early twenties. She wore her hair up, her skirts short and her heels high. She had become Mrs Tanner on 4 October at the Registry Office on Rosamund Street. It was a shot-gun wedding with her father making sure that Arnold turned up. Arthur Grimshaw was more than happy to have the cheeky, thankless girl off his hands once and for all.

Neither Tanner pretended to love the other. Elsie's pregnancy and subsequent marriage were a result of a drunken party, and they both agreed to make the most of the situation. To Elsie, this meant the opportunity to start her own home away from the slum that she had grown up in on Gas Street. Situated next to the workhouse, the tenement block that the twelve Grimshaws lived in had been condemned as long ago as 1894 — but it was still standing and was still occupied.

As Elsie started to make her plans to feather her newly acquired nest, Arnold made his own plans — to get as far away from Elsie as possible. The day after they moved in, Arnold left with his unpacked bags to join the Royal Navy to serve his King and country.

The people of Coronation Street showed no friendship towards the young Mrs Tanner. Their minds were too occupied with the thought of the homeless widow from Wright Street. After receiving many awkward stares and ignored greetings, Elsie's reaction was just to laugh and light up a cigarette. The residents kept up their silent treatment towards the outsider until the night of 10 January 1940. The realization that her baby was on the way caused Elsie to burst into the public bar at the Rovers Return and demand some help. In the confusion that followed, Elsie forged lifelong friendships with the residents and gave birth to a daughter, Linda, in publican Annie Walker's living room.

Arnold Tanner paid a photographer to get his wedding photograph in the local paper. Little did he suspect that less than a year later his disillusioned 16-year-old bride Elsie would cut him out of the picture.

At the Town Hall, Albert Tatlock was moved from the housing department to help with the compilation of a register of all Weatherfield inhabitants. He had just finished the register for Coronation Street when he had to make an addition: his neighbour, Ida Barlow, gave birth on 9 October and she named her first son Kenneth.

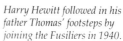 IDA LEFT ALL ALONE

'I can make and mend. I've always been able to, I've always had to. That doesn't mean to say I like doing so.'

Ida Barlow hated the war. She felt tormented by the laughter and smiles

Harry Hewitt followed in his father Thomas' footsteps by joining the Fusiliers in 1940.

Whilst Ida Barlow sat at home waiting for news of her soldier husband Frank, toddler David nearly suffocated by unthreading his blanket and sticking the wool up his nose.

that seemed to be present in her neighbours' lives — she just felt so alone. Isolated from all she held dear, she found her vulnerability as a woman bringing up children alone very frightening. The sense of despair she had experienced after Kenneth's birth was intensified with the birth of her second son, David, in 1942.

Rationing was impossible to cope with and to keep track of, and the everyday tasks that Frank would have performed so easily took on mammoth proportions. The window, nailed-up because of a broken sash, made her feel guilty every time she looked at it.

At night, sleeping with the boys for comfort, Ida missed Frank's reassuring voice and as the bombs fell she longed for his support and hand to hold. Churchill's speeches caused no patriotic stirrings within her; Vera Lynn's songs held no promises.

If Frank returned alive, would his spirit be as broken as her father's had been after the Great War? Everything had been altered, distorted and broken. Security was a luxury Ida could not afford and she couldn't help wondering if things would ever be the same again.

Ida had refused to be evacuated with the other expectant mothers. The evacuation of school children, pregnant women, mothers with small children and the blind had started during August. At the time Ida had agreed with her husband Frank that war would never be declared, and even if it was it would be over by Christmas, so there was no point in leaving the city. May Hardman did not share her optimism. Taking the first chance she had, she fled Weatherfield with her baby Christine for the safety of the coast.

At Bessie Street School, Ada Hayes joined her fellow teachers in accompanying the children in their care to the railway stations to be sent off to their unknown destinations. The children of Bessie Street were to spend the majority of the war safely billeted at St Anne's and Blackpool, a bit further north. When she arrived, Beattie Tatlock hurriedly wrote an excited letter home with the news that her new bedroom boasted a wonderful view of Blackpool Tower.

Rationing started in earnest at the beginning of 1941. Like many small shopkeepers, Tommy Foyle found himself becoming unpopular with his regulars as he had to bring into force the new rules and regulations over food allocation. Some women would wait until his wife Elsie was serving before entering the shop, in the hope that she would show some extra kindness when handing out eggs or sugar.

Annie Walker, ever watchful of budget increases, caused an outcry by putting the price of the already rationed beer up by one penny a pint. Tommy Foyle stopped buying whisky from the pub when it was increased by one shilling and nine pence a bottle to 16 shillings. He joined the increasing number of people knocking on Frank Jackson's door to see what black-market wares he had on offer.

The streets of Weatherfield emptied of young men as they signed up or were conscripted into service. For the first time, women came out of the Snug and occupied the public bar at the Rovers. The months of war soon dragged into years. With many of the men away, those left did all they could to help the war effort. Ena Sharples found time in her crowded day to take a job in munitions, welding breech blocks onto rifles. She persuaded her friend Martha Longhurst to join her but had no such luck with fellow widow, Minnie Caldwell, who stayed at home nursing her mother, who was bedridden with shock after narrowly escaping a German bomb. Many other women of the time signed up to do their bit for their country by working in munitions factories.

Tommy and Elsie Foyle's daughter Hilda enjoyed her stay in Blackpool where she had been evacuated with her sister Shelagh in 1939.

☙ BETTY PRESTON AND A LOVE ☙ THAT TURNED SOUR

'I may well look back at this period in my life and smile with the memory, but now I'm crying with the pain.'

When asked by strangers which house on Tile Street was occupied by the Prestons, residents would nod towards the green door at Number 6 and remark 'there, the loveless house'. This comment was unkind to the house's residents, but was a predictable response from neighbours used to receiving sour looks from 'Holy Harold' and frightened glances from the women in his family. The sight of Harold Preston, walking with the aid of his elephant-handled cane, his back permanently bent crooked, and the tails of his black coat flapping open, struck terror into the hearts of local children.

In reality, Harold was a normal man like the neighbours he never socialized with, a tram driver promoted to the position of Inspector, he was a strict puritan, even to the point of refusing to allow his wife Margaret to hang their daughters' undergarments out in public. He never drank, but always sang in the choir and read aloud from the Bible for an hour every night to his two daughters.

Betty had never meant to rebel against her inhibited upbringing, and she actually quite enjoyed living with a masterful father. Unlike her sister

21-year-old Betty Preston was employed at a munitions factory in 1941, much against her father's wishes.

Maggie, who was quiet and reserved, Betty had inherited all Harold's forthright, stubborn and bossy qualities. She understood that her father's strictness stemmed from his worry that his daughters' youthful innocence would be contaminated by the harsh outside world.

April 1941 heralded a major change in Betty's life. Like all 21-year-old women, she was forced to register for war work. Harold used what little influence he had to secure her a job in the Food Office. For the first time in her life, Betty clashed with her father. She refused to work in the 'safety' of an office and signed up for munition work.

Whilst Maggie was forced to work in the Food Office, Betty settled down to life at Earnshaw's factory. Her eyes were opened to attitudes and expressions that at first shocked and then amused her. She loved the early morning scramble at 8am as the day and night shifts jostled for space through the same door. With only three minutes allowed for clocking in on time, Betty used her ample frame to push her way into the works. Placed in charge of a drilling machine, Betty's job was to drill holes into sheets of metal by using a lever. For security reasons, she never knew what it was she was helping to make.

At first, Betty felt certain she would die of boredom sitting at the same machine for ten hours a day. She soon found, however, that the hours flew by as she listened avidly to the conversations of her fellow workers. She learnt all the popular songs and joined in the swaying when singing *Boogie Woogie Bugle Boy*.

Corporal Ted Farrell was stationed in Manchester. He was a native of Portsmouth and was having difficulty adjusting to life in the industrial North. Resorting to the tried and tested mode of entertainment, the cinema, he found himself queuing outside the Bijou in Weatherfield to see *To Have and Have Not*. Standing immediately in front of him was a young woman who was humming the theme tune from the film. He asked her if she had seen it before, and when she said she had, he replied that so had he. He then gave his impersonation of Humphrey Bogart. Betty laughed and as soon as he heard her voice he felt he wanted to get to know her.

Corporal Ted Farrell was a Southerner; he fell for Betty Preston and kept from her the fact that he was already married.

Walking Betty home after the film, Ted told her all about himself and arranged to see her again the next evening. For the first time in three years, Betty had something to tell the girls as she sat down to her drilling machine the next morning — the news that Betty had her own feller spread quickly around the room.

All too soon, Ted was sent away to fight abroad. After four months of exchanging letters, Betty suddenly found hers were being unanswered. Resigning herself to the fact that Ted obviously had decided to forget her, Betty was saddened as she found her feelings for him were growing.

The end of the war held little excitement for Betty. Free from working at the factory, she soon lost contact with her chums at work. Days of mending and washing awaited her at home. Betty took a job as an usherette at the Bijou and enviously followed Maggie's romance with sailor Les Clegg as it blossomed into engagement. And then Ted returned home.

Now working as a sales representative, Ted told Betty that he had thought he would never see her again. Since their last meeting he had served a year as a prisoner of war abroad. He had never forgotten her and was desperate to start again. Love soon blossomed for the young couple and they picked up from where they'd left off.

Betty followed Maggie down the aisle knowing she was pregnant. Her carefully placed bridesmaid's bouquet hid any signs and she kept a permanent smile on her face. While Maggie and Les were on honeymoon, Betty's prayers that Harold wouldn't notice her anguish were answered in a morbid way when he was killed by a Number 14 tram.

Ted's response to Betty's news of her pregnancy was not what she had expected. Rather than delight, his face showed horror, instead of embracing her he backed off. Betty felt ashamed by his reactions and guilt and hurt overwhelmed her. To Betty's horror Ted broke down in tears. She had never seen a man cry before. He explained that he couldn't marry her as he already had a wife in Portsmouth. He promised to sort things out, get a divorce and marry her then, but that would take time.

As soon as Ted had gone, Betty knew he would never return. She wrote to his firm, telling him she had lost the baby and that she understood his position. She had not really lost the baby but Maggie had lost hers. As Maggie was told she could never have children, Betty saw the solution to her problem. The Cleggs agreed with her that they could adopt the child and bring it up as their own. With the knowledge that she would be an aunt to her own child, Betty left Weatherfield with the Cleggs to start a new life in Birmingham.

All the rules and regulations that had been such a nuisance at the beginning of the war became extremely helpful when the Germans started blitzing Manchester. Ground level air-raid shelters had been constructed all over Weatherfield as only two per cent of the houses had gardens. Unlike the Londoners, the people of Weatherfield had no underground stations to shelter in so they turned to the abundance of factory and mill basements for shelter. The Government built brick shelters in the streets, but they were often overcrowded and sanitation was impossible. The people of Coronation Street and Victoria Street were allocated places in the shelter situated in the Mission of Glad Tidings' basement.

Ena Sharples, in her role of caretaker, kept the shelter clean and collected a good supply of blankets from the local ladies. For the duration of the blitz, the Coronation Street residents became well organized in their nightly routine. Elliston's factory hooter was fitted with a siren and this signalled an air-raid. ARP Albert Tatlock shepherded the neighbours into the shelter after his wife had gone ahead to get the prime place by the boiler. The residents descending into the basement were met by Ena in her ARP helmet who gave them coloured chalk. Each family placed its belongings on the floor and chalked round their spaces. This was meant to be for identification purposes if the Mission was to suffer a direct hit. Much as Ena's bossy manner annoyed the residents, her calmness and authority were comforting and her fine singing voice, leading them all in popular songs, helped to while away the tense hours.

Weatherfield suffered severe bombardment during the blitz with the houses between Rosamund Street and Upper Edward Street being completely demolished. The tenement blocks on Gas Street, long due for slum clearance, were demolished overnight by the Luftwaffe. Elsie Tanner lost both her parents, a brother and six sisters in that particular raid. The houses and warehouses surrounding the docks to the south of town were also badly hit by the bombers, as were Marshall's Cotton Mill and the Gas Works. Miraculously the houses and businesses in the heart of Weatherfield were saved. The Infirmary, St Mary's and Rosamund Street were hardly touched by the bombers.

While the houses on Coronation Street remained unscathed, its residents did not. Sally Todd had to have her head shaved because of the wounds she suffered after being caught in an explosion. Jack Walker, home on leave, returned to the army with his left leg stitched from top to bottom after glass fragments hit him. 64-year-old Sid Hayes, returning home from a Mission meeting, was caught in an air raid and took refuge in the Gas Street shelter just before it suffered a direct hit. The news of her husband's death was brought to Alice Hayes by a policeman. As the air raids continued the shelters all over Weatherfield were in constant use.

≈ HILDA MEETS HER STAN ≈

'Well Stanley, that's another fine mess you've got me into!'

Air raid sirens brought out the true sprinter in Hilda Crabtree. The sound of their first screech caused a reaction in her similar to that of a pistol's crack on a sports field. She had memorized the exact locations of all the Weatherfield air shelters and knew those that were damp and those which tended to be overcrowded. She always avoided the shelter under the Mission of Glad Tidings as the warden was so bossy and she also gave a wide berth to the smelly glue factory shelter.

On the night of 1 December 1943, Hilda was returning home to Kitchener Street after an evening spent at the Tripe Dressers Arms with boyfriend Sgt Harry Battersby. Harry's attempts to get her drunk had backfired as she had poured her drinks into his glass when he wasn't looking. After supporting him back home to his mother's, Hilda found she was a mile away from home.

It was just as she left Gladstone Terrace that the siren started. As Hilda automatically ducked to avoid any falling debris, the lights started to go out. She ran in darkness down Upper Edward Street, her heels clashing noisily on the cobbles. At one point she dropped her green felt hat and lit a match to locate it. A warden shouted angrily, 'Put that light out,' just as she burnt her finger on the offending match. Knowing the Crimea Street shelter under the tailoring factory was nearest, Hilda turned the corner by the Co-op at speed. It was then that she tripped over an old bundle of clothes on the pavement and smashed down on top of it.

Having won the Docker's Arms pint drinking contest five years running, Stanley Josiah Ogden had been proclaimed the drinking man's champion in Dock Street. Now, as Private Ogden 842 he cursed the fact that not only was beer scarce, but eight months in the Western Desert had rendered him capable of being paralytic after a measly six-pub crawl. As he sat, propping up the Co-op wall, planning how to spend the rest of his four-day leave, a limping, doubled-up figure suddenly knocked into him and brutally winded him by sticking a foot in his stomach.

So it was that Hilda and Stan first met each other and fell in love. The

Stan Ogden narrowly escaped death during the war when an ambulance he was driving came under enemy fire.

love aspect did not start at once. Hilda's immediate reaction was to flee to the awaiting shelter, away from the horrible beer-sodden tramp. The fact that her heel was trapped in Stan's belt made this act impossible and she froze as Stan lit a match. As their eyes met, Stan saw a thin, smartly dressed woman in a green two-piece who resembled his favourite aunt Cissy. Hilda could hardly believe her eyes as the bundle of clothes turned out to be more like the film star Clark Gable. She helped him to his feet and he followed her into the shelter. Hilda was just about to announce she had found her screen idol when the light of the shelter revealed that she was wrong. Besides, she should have known Californian Clark wouldn't have greeted her with such a greeting as 'Ello chuck'.

During the air raid, Stan sobered up and enjoyed the way Hilda never seemed to stop talking about herself, her family and life as an embalmer's daughter. She gave him her cup of tea when the flasks were handed round and decided that even if he wasn't Clark, he was the nearest thing she was going to get to him.

Six days later, by special licence, Hilda and Stan were married. She wore a two-piece with padded shoulders. He wore his uniform. The reception at the Spinners' Arms was disturbed by the arrival of Joan Fairhurst who announced that the groom was her fiancée. Stan's best man Bernie Sparks solved the embarrassing problem by proposing to Joan himself on the condition that she kept the engagement ring Stan had bought her.

After the reception, Stan carried Hilda's cases from Kitchener Street down to his family home in Mare Street. It was there, in his mother's bedroom (she was visiting relatives in Blackpool) that the newlyweds spent their wedding night together. Their brief moment of happiness was shattered the next morning when the Military Police arrived and arrested Stan for over-staying his leave. Mary Ogden returned home to find that she had a new resident daughter-in-law.

Hilda allowed Mary to pamper her after announcing her pregnancy. She enjoyed being the centre of attention and, on discovering she wasn't pregnant after all, decided not to tell Mary it was a false alarm. Three months passed before Mary discovered her deception. Her reaction was to throw Hilda out and to tell her never to return.

Hilda spent the rest of the war at her new rented home in 17 Charles Street. Stan returned on leave twice and left her pregnant on both occasions. Her mother Florence looked after the babies, Sylvia and Tony, while Hilda worked hard in the munitions factory. Stan enjoyed the remainder of the war as a POW in an Italian camp where he captained the football team.

Hilda Crabtree was only 19 when she met and married Stan Ogden. At the time she was working in a munitions factory.

Despite the long-term absence of their menfolk, the local women continued to give birth to wartime babies. In Coronation Street, Joan Walker, David Barlow and Dennis Tanner were all the results of their

Like so many local girls, aircraft fitter Sally Todd fell in love with an American GI. Their love survived the war and she went to live with him in America.

fathers' leave from various forces. Sally Todd had no father's name to give her son Clark when he was born in 1944. Sally, like so many women in the area, had fallen for the good looks of an American GI based at Burtonwood. Clark was the result of her passionate relationship with Oliver Hart. The Todd family had met Oliver during his time in England and had grown to like him. This was mainly due to his generosity with rationed goods which he brought with him on his visits. Faced with Sally's pregnancy, the Todds, unlike many families in the same situation, stood by their daughter and Clark was delivered into the world by Vi herself.

⇒ DOT TODD GOES 'YANKING' ⇐

'If I'm being called a "good-time girl" I might as well 'ave a good time!'

The USAAF van parked outside the Bijou Cinema on Rosamund Street always pulled away full to the brim of local women. The fragile cargo was driven at high speed to Warrington, joining identical vans journeying away from Manchester. At the 8th Air Force Base Air Depot, Burtonwood, hundreds of American soldiers and airforce technicians waited impatiently for the vans bringing the Weatherfield girls, who were eager to dance and to romance the night away.

Elsie Tanner and the Todd sisters never travelled to the air base in the vans. They were the envy of local women as they had secured for themselves the first three GIs to enter Weatherfield looking for entertainment. Since then they had had their own escorts to the Base dances and always travelled in army jeeps.

Gregory Flint came from Chicago. His passionate romance with Dot Todd came to an end when she turned him down in favour of Walter Greenhalgh.

Master Sgt Gregg Flint, 22, of the USA Air Force, was Dot's latest conquest. Armed with a maturity beyond her 19 years, Dot had won his affections by refusing his first three approaches and submitting herself, coyly, at his fourth. Elsie hadn't even waited for Lee Kuhlman's second pass before she gave in to him.

Dot had decided that the only way to get through a war that left her without stockings and weary from making uniforms all day was to enjoy herself with the visiting forces. Her first visit to Burtonwood had been with neighbour Elsie when, dressed as WAAFs, they had gatecrashed a show given by Bob Hope. Since that night both girls had rarely spent a Saturday night alone.

An American jeep parked outside the Rovers Return became a regular sight in the last years of the war. Annie Walker enjoyed the GI's company and positively flirted with them, with the bar top safely between herself and the Yanks. Ida Barlow and Esther Hayes were embarrassed by the Americans' coarseness, while Ena Sharples told Elsie Tanner exactly what she thought of her for making her children sit eating chips on the doorstep whilst she entertained her fellers inside.

Although engaged to factory fitter Walt Greenhalgh, Dot refused to be tied down. Walter was serving overseas and might never return, and Dot wanted to have a good time while she could. Rationing did not suit girls like Dot; her usually rounded figure appeared lumpy in old mended dresses. Hands used for stitching uniforms needed to be pampered and Gregg easily spent his money on lotions and stockings for his 'gal'.

Dot was pleased when Elsie took up with Gregg's pal Steve Tanner. They met for the first time in Cheshire, at the Roebuck Inn. With a terrible

Len Fairclough served in the Navy alongside Walt Greenhalgh. They had become friends at school when the Faircloughs had moved from their native Liverpool, and Len was the natural choice to be Walt's best man when he married Dot Todd.

joke about getting change for a bob, Gregg had introduced Tanner to Tanner. Elsie had spent the rest of the evening staring into the eyes of a tall, dark, confident American with film-star looks. Over the next few months Gregg and Steve spent all their spare time in Weatherfield. Elsie realized that she was falling in love for the first time in her life, and cursed her fate for securing her lot as a married mother.

Before he returned to America, Steve asked Elsie to wait for him to return for her, so she and the children could join him in America. Elsie asked him not to return as she had decided to give her marriage as good an attempt as she could. She may have been branded a slut by the local matrons, but she had never removed her wedding ring and was determined to be a good wife and mother when her husband Arnold returned.

Dot decided to remain in England for much the same reasons. Gregg had proposed, even bought a ring, but out of some traditional sense of 'keeping home fires burning', Dot had turned him down. Walt didn't have film-star looks, or a sexy accent or any money, but he was safe, sensible and reliable and was the sort of man she had always known she would marry.

Vi Todd saved the family's coupons for four months in order to buy Dot a new dress when she married Walt. Although marrying on leave from the Navy, Walt disappointed his bride by not marrying in uniform. Elsie, attending the service, was surprised and pleased to find her old schooldays' boyfriend Len Fairclough serving as Walt's best man.

Madge Mason house-sat for her sister May Hardman at Number 13 for the duration of the war.

Weatherfield survived all the atrocities that war had to throw at it: rationing, bombing, isolation and death. In Coronation Street, as in thousands of Manchester streets, the announcement that the Allies had been victorious sparked off a spontaneous party. The streets of Weatherfield sang again with the voices of young children who had sheltered out of the city for the duration of the hostilities. For some there were no homes to return to, some returned as strangers to their families, while others brought home new customs and accents. Beattie Tatlock returned after an absence of six years and was no longer a shy little six-year-old, but a poised twelve-year-old. Under the influence of her professional foster parents, Beattie appeared well educated and had obviously grown used to life in their grand detached house. For Beattie Coronation Street was not a welcome sight.

The men returned from fighting to find that 'the little wives' they had left behind had turned into independent working women who had learnt how to cope and survive on their own. Many Weatherfield women refused to give up the independence they had grown accustomed to, and ,moving off munitions, took jobs which had previously been dominated by men. Elsie Tanner, looking forward to giving up working, was struck by life's irony when her husband

The Todd family was split apart at the end of the war. Mother Vi (left) died and Sally (right) went to live in America, whilst her sister Dot settled into 18 Victoria Street as Mrs Walter Greenhalgh.

Arnold announced he was staying in the Navy and left immediately for sea. At this stage she didn't realize her marriage was over and that she wasn't to see him again for another 15 years.

Sally Todd waved goodbye to England at the Liverpool docks and, clutching baby Clark to her, cried with her fellow GI Brides before setting off for a new life in America where her new husband awaited her. Only Dot and her father Jack were at the quay side to see Sally off. World War Two had ravaged their family. Her younger brother Jim had been killed in action in Burma and her mother Vi had died of pneumonia, brought on by spending endless nights in a damp shelter.

While the residents of Coronation Street sang along to Ena's piano playing in the Mission hall, the Victory celebrations spread across Weatherfield. Church bells rang out for the first time in four years, lights blared out of windows and car horns blasted triumphantly. Tommy Foyle, watching the street party from his bedroom window, did not enjoy it for long as he suffered a fatal heart attack. At Number 11 two Americans held a banner out of Elsie's bedroom window — it read 'God Bless Monty and the Lads'.

CHAPTER 7

1945-1960:
WE'VE NEVER HAD IT SO GOOD

Elsie Tanner in a provocative pose modelling a ball gown for her employers, Miami Modes. She started work in the dress shop in 1955.

THOSE WHO RETURNED to civilian life — Civvy Street — in 1945 and 1946 returned to a totally different world from their less fortunate predecessors returning from World War One.

For a start, every man was either given a smart demob outfit of suit, shirt, tie, shoes and hat or a sum of money in lieu. They also had a much more buoyant and enlightened private life to return to as their women were freed from the Victorian restrictions that had held them back before the war. The women were also now more skilled away from the home because of their hard work for the war effort and they were certainly more self aware than before.

American films had flourished during the war and had featured emancipated beauties like Betty Grable, Rita Hayworth and Veronica Lake, who provided the women with sophisticated role models to admire and imitate.

For most ex-servicemen there was a job available either in their old firm or within the major re-building programme that was needed because of the destructive work of the Luftwaffe. But not all immediately found a suitable position, and it was harder for those who stayed on to sort things out after VE Day in May 1945. It was tougher still for those who operated in the Far East and whose war dragged on till VJ Day on 6 August 1945, when Japan admitted defeat after the dropping of the Atomic bomb.

⇒ PERCY LEAVES THE ARMY ⇐

'When you've made gravy under gun fire, no task is too much.'

Percy Sugden left the army, none too willingly, in late 1945. No sooner had the German surrender been announced than preparations to return to Civvy Street were underway. But Percy was reluctant to give up the niche he had carved for himself in the field cookhouse in Libya.

He arrived back in Weatherfield one Sunday morning with a sun tan, a brown chalk-stripe demob suit, just a little too small for him, and a suitcase containing his spoils of war collected during his time in Egypt and North Africa as a member of the Catering Corps.

Percy had been due to return with his regiment in early 1945 but had gladly agreed to stay on as a Sergeant batman at the request of his former CO, Colonel Simpson, who had seen Percy in action and wished to keep his services till he had closed down the regiment's operations at the British base.

For that last year, Percy had thrived on the authority his promotion had brought him. While Colonel Simpson spent his days 'tidying up', Percy compiled lists, made out requisitions and ran the Housey-Housey game every night at the Buffs Club.

Returning to Weatherfield, Percy soon found he had no forms to sign, no bodies to manipulate and he had to look for a suitable job for his skills. With so many servicemen already back and on the market, Percy spent many weeks pursuing jobs that had already been taken. With funds running out and no job in sight, he found it necessary to live on a tight budget at Number 5 Booth Street, his family home, which had lain empty since 1943 when his parents moved to the Lakes to avoid the bombing.

They had continued to pay the rent in Percy's absence as Millie, his elder sister, had chosen to stay in Weatherfield. She had married returning serviceman Walter Prior in 1945 and moved away to a new home in Leeds. Percy was now king of a vacant castle but he soon tired of his empty days and boring nights.

His twenty-fourth birthday in early 1946 saw him still jobless with just one pound two and eight pence in his pocket and a smart suit which now fitted him perfectly due to his restricted diet.

However, fortune smiled on him when he met a former army colleague from the army cookhouse who had found work at Holmes Bakery in Upper Edward Street. He told Percy there was a vacancy for a pastry cook which would be ideal for him.

Percy acted immediately and went straight up to Cyril Holmes' office to tell Cyril of his good fortune in having available the services of Sergeant Percy Sugden late of the Catering Corps. Percy told him he would not only take over from his retiring pastry cook, but bring a new quality and individuality to the uninspired Holmes range. He explained that he had spent some time studying their shop window and impressed Cyril Holmes enough for him to offer Percy a job on the spot. Percy started next day on two pounds ten shillings a week.

He soon got to grips with the work and there was no doubt that the quality and variety of Holmes' delicacies improved under Percy's direction. While his colleagues scoffed at his hard work Percy prospered and soon advanced to assistant manager. Percy loved his work; once again

Young Percy Sugden struggled to find a job and was eventually taken on by Holmes Bakery. He was rewarded in 1952 when he was made general manager.

he began to feel his importance and revel in the power a white coat and clipboard could bring.

At first romance escaped Percy, as his off-duty pursuits were mainly in all-male company and at work the young women showed him respect to his face but were very disrespectful behind his back.

However, Mary Jackson from the fancies counter was flattered by comments about her talents with icing and marzipan and began to be very friendly towards him. Percy responded to this and asked her to join him at the bandstand in the park on the next Sunday, at 15.00 hours. She arrived precisely on time, and told him that she'd learnt punctuality in the WAAF. Percy was even more respectful when he realized he was dealing with an ex-servicewoman.

When he visited her parents' home in Lime Avenue the following week and found her not only to be an excellent cook, but also the possessor of a budgie called Bertie, he suddenly realized he had found his life's companion and proposed the very same day. They married in November 1946 and went to Morecambe for their honeymoon.

Things had worked out well for Percy. He was twenty-four years old, had a neat little home in Booth Street and a wife who loved him, despite his officious tendencies — in fact she loved him the more for them.

At the bakery, he now ruled the roost, reporting only to Cyril Holmes who was quite happy to leave the day-to-day running of things to his highly efficient and hard-working lieutenant. It was one of the proudest days of Percy's life when, finally, he arrived back from a summer holiday in Rhyll in 1952 to find a brass nameplate on his office door proclaiming: 'P. Sugden — General Manager'.

Although Percy and Mary had no children of their own they doted on their nieces Elaine and Frances, seen here with them on a day out to Morecambe.

As the new Labour government under Mr Atlee fulfilled its election promises and the welfare state began to take shape, Weatherfield settled back to enjoy the strange new world of 'Father Feed 'em All' where everyone was looked after by the state. In the Rovers, the new jukebox, installed much against Annie Walker's principles, offered a definite attraction to the well-off American GIs, and replaced the usual quiet conversation with the melodies of Glen Miller and the well-known wartime harmonies of the Andrews Sisters. In spite of her abject dislike for this sort of music, Annie smiled sweetly and bore the noise as she changed yet another pound note for a happy American serviceman buying drinks all round. What she *did* object

:o, though, was her son Billy's obsession with the machine and his frequent visits to it during closing hours.

⇘ BILLY WALKER GETS EXPELLED ⇙

'There are Walkers and there are Walkers and I'm afraid I'm never going to be your genial inn keeper like me dad and me mum. I think I could well turn out to be the family black sheep.'

Billy Walker, never happy with the silver spoon in his mouth, failed to live up to his mother's high expectations of him. After expulsion from Mrs Henderson's posh private academy he returned to Bessie Street School.

Billy Walker did not ask to be associated with the Clitheroe Beaumonts, his mother's family, but Annie Walker insisted that his early upbringing should be suited to a family of some status.

Annie was, in her opinion, culturally above her regulars at the Rovers Return and, for that matter, above her own husband Jack. None of them had been Clitheroe Beaumonts nor possessed the inbred refinement that Annie felt she exuded with her every expression and gesture.

When Billy commenced his secondary education, he reported to the local Bessie Street Seniors with blazer, cap and even a satchel in such an immaculate state that the headmaster, Mr Pope, suspected that he had arrived at the wrong school and should have been reporting to the posh Henderson's Private School.

Annie had escorted Billy right to the school gates but had withdrawn, albeit reluctantly, when Billy had objected to standing next to the well-dressed lady in a fox fur while his new companions reported in far less perfect order and with poorer looking mothers. As they waited to be registered, Billy was quite relieved to find himself sitting next to Kenneth Barlow from Coronation Street, who was almost as well turned out as he was but somehow bore the burden with less shame. However hard he tried, Billy could never get on that well with Kenneth, who was far too straight-laced and serious and paid little or no attention to the *Beano* which Billy always carried in his back pocket to read surreptitiously in a quiet moment.

On the whole, though, things didn't seem too bad for Billy as he surveyed his class of schoolmates. They weren't all like Kenneth Barlow and there were quite a few of the boys that Billy had met in the park that summer. Also, he found himself sitting close to Chris-

Jack and Annie Walker ran the Rovers Return for over 30 years until June 1970.

tine Hardman from down the street, who was really pretty. His mother, Annie, on the other hand found things less than satisfactory as Billy returned from school each day in a progressively more dishevelled state and with a rapidly expanding vocabulary of bad language.

To her horror, Annie realized Billy was beginning to sound like those other dreadful 'common' children. Billy's stay at Bessie Street finally came to an abrupt end when he was brought home by a policeman with numerous bleeding cuts, after he had fallen through a cucumber frame while scrumping apples from a garden in Oakhill.

The very next day Billy was taken by Annie to Mrs Dudley Henderson's Private Academy in Cloister Street where he was kitted out with his new school uniform and located in his new class the same day. Annie felt much happier with this arrangement, even though the £15 a term fee took some finding. She couldn't wait to tell Jack that not only had some of the pupils arrived by motor car but that one of them had been Eric Pickles whose father was the soft-furnishings manager at Kendall-Milne.

At first, Billy felt out of place among the more serious-minded fellow pupils he now found about him but, never lacking in self confidence, he soon established a little coterie of friends that he could control with just a flick of his little finger.

Far from Annie's dream of Billy being influenced by his peers to become a studious, law-abiding scholar bound for academic success, the reverse happened and Billy managed to bring quite a few well-behaved friends down to his level. Billy's little gang, more resourceful than their counterparts at Bessie Street, ruled the roost at the Academy and managed in less than three months to bring disrepute to an establishment whose reputation had previously been untarnished throughout its seven years of existence.

The end to Billy's stay there was not long in coming. During the Easter holidays of 1952, Annie received a letter, beautifully embossed with the Academy crest, in which Donald Henderson, Deputy Headmaster, praised Billy's spirit and acumen but thought his education might be furthered better at a more *suitable* school.

Annie dropped the letter on the breakfast table as though it had burned her fingers. There was no doubting the wording, Billy had been expelled! Across the table, Billy dunked his soldiers in his egg unaware that the wrath of Annie was about to descend upon him. Jack was called in from his work at the beer pumps and Billy's young sister Joan was sent from the room.

Billy would long remember the inquisition that followed as he tried to recall why Mr Henderson had taken such a hard line. There *was* the fire in the dustbin and Mrs Jones the RI teacher *had* been bruised, but she had quickly recovered from her fall and Shirley Jennings from 2 Classical did *not* always tell the real truth. Not to be defeated, Annie probed further until

Billy eventually admitted the fight with sneaky Sol Simon in the last assembly, for which both had been severely and publicly caned, which *might* have occasioned the Deputy Headmaster's action.

Billy returned to Bessie Street to finish his last year of education. Annie endeavoured to cover up the true facts by saying that she had voluntarily removed Billy from the Academy to bring him back to his roots and make him more aware of his near neighbours. Billy was welcomed back by his old pals at Bessie Street as he told stories of his adventures in the 'posh' school from which he had emerged unscathed.

The presence of the US servicemen who stayed on after 1945 was a delight to all the good-time girls and free-loaders who shamelessly accepted their generosity in order to enjoy the luxuries they, like every other British citizen, had been starved of during the war years. But to the returning servicemen like Len Fairclough, Alf Roberts and Harry Hewitt, the GIs' affluence, smart uniforms and attractive accents presented an unfair challenge.

⧢ HARRY HEWITT'S TRAGEDY ⧢

'I can't bring a child up. Lucille needs a mother. I'm no good with 'er and she knows it. Sometimes I think she 'ates me for it.'

Harry Hewitt was a bus conductor who lived alone at Number 7 Coronation Street after his father, Thomas, died in 1947. In the main, Harry kept himself to himself, apart from the odd visit to the Rovers and the occasional night out with his fellow employees from the Weatherfield Bus Company, where he had worked since leaving the Lancashire Fusiliers in 1946.

The Hewitt family had never really recovered from the disgrace of Harry's mother, Mary, being taken away in a plain van, after she attacked Harry with a knife and pursued him into the street ranting and raving. Remaining in a mentally unstable state until her death she had not returned home and her husband Thomas had not lingered long after her departure.

Harry was left alone with his pipe, his whippets and little else until in 1948 he met and married a fellow employee, clippie Lizzie Harding. They found a common bond in loneliness — her parents had both been killed by a bomb in the war — and married as much from convenience as great passion.

Their daughter, Lucille, was born in 1949 and unlike the previous Mrs Hewitt, Lizzie was a caring and dutiful parent. Under her guidance, young Lucille wanted for nothing and was always a well-turned-out and polite little girl.

Maison Bridget
Styles for the Fifties
57 VICTORIA STREET
Phone for Appointment
Weatherfield 2362

Maison Bridget, established in 1948 by Bridget Menton — who arrived in England as a refugee from war-torn Paris — offered cheap cuts, Marcel waving and 'the most stylish coiffure in Weatherfield'. The doors were closed in 1959 when the 'Bouffant', 'Beehive' and other, to Bridget, outrageous styles of the Sixties emerged.

Money was so short in the Hewitt house that for a year Harry and Lizzie used a bedroom door as a table.

JIFFY DYES

27 LOVELY COLOURS
SWINDLEYS
EMPORIUM
16 ROSAMUND STREET
WEATHERFIELD
Telephone 2888

*After the war, clothes rationing
continued for some time. To keep
up with fashion, and to save
money, the clients of Swindley's
Emporium were obliged to resort
to re-styling and dyeing the
existing stock.*

*Alice Burgess, Harry Hewitt's
widowed sister, came to help
Harry after his wife's death, but
could not get on with her niece,
Lucille, or Harry's whippets.*

At that time, Lucille was the only young child in the street and as such enjoyed the attentions and kindnesses of the older residents who always had a cheery word for her and sometimes gave her sweets or pocket money.

Harry had every reason to be a happy man. At the bus station, he had ten years service to look back on and was next in line for promotion. At home, he had a family to be proud of and a pair of whippets that already promised success at Belle Vue and the other venues where they ran.

He also had a good friend in local handyman Len Fairclough, who had left the Navy in 1946 and who shared his interest in his dogs and the local pub, the Rovers. The two men were a similar age and Len's son Stanley went to Bessie Street School at the same time as Lucille. The only regret Harry had about his friendship with Len was Len's ability to get into arguments that usually ended in blows.

In January 1959 misfortune touched the ill-fated Hewitts once again when a bus skidded on the icy road in Rosamund Street, mounted the pavement and killed Lizzie instantly. Harry was at the garage, dressing to go home, when the driver returned, trembling with shock, to tell everyone what had happened. As Harry comforted the distraught man, he little realized that he was hearing of his own wife's death as the man blurted out all the terrifying details.

When grim-faced Ena Sharples answered his door with an arm around a sobbing Lucille, he knew immediately the news that he was about to hear. The neighbours rallied round and did all they could. Elsie Lappin, who ran the corner shop delivered boxes of food and Esther Hayes from Number 5 volunteered to do their washing and tidy up the house. Harry's widowed sister, Alice Burgess, came to keep house for the distressed pair, but unable to get on with Lucille, she returned to her home in Birmingham.

On a temporary basis, everything was going well, but Lucille's schooling was severely affected by Lizzie's absence. Reluctantly, Harry was obliged to apply to the Council for Lucille to be taken into care. He tried to explain that it was only for a short time that she would be away, only until he got things sorted out, but Lucille knew she faced life in a home until she was old enough to leave school.

She refused to leave their home, saying that she was quite capable of looking after herself and pleading with Harry not to let her leave. Once the care order had been put in action, Harry was powerless, and inevitably the morning for Lucille's departure came. The lady who came from the children's home, Mrs Shuttleworth, was kind and sympathetic, but somehow Harry experienced more grief at Lucille's leaving than he had at his wife's death.

Lucille pleaded not to go and cried and then screamed in anguish as her bag was loaded into the car boot and she and Mrs Shuttleworth were packed into the back seat by the solemn-faced driver. Harry was never to forget the vision of Lucille's distressed face as she looked back at him through the small rear window of the car as it pulled out of Coronation Street.

She would be back, he was sure, but Harry Hewitt was lonelier and more miserable than he had ever been in his life as he watched the car turn into Rosamund Street and he returned to the empty, cheerless Number 7.

≋

Lucille's distress and Harry's sorrow were deeply felt by one of Harry's drinking pals from the Rovers, Alf Roberts, who had experienced family bereavement himself, and was well aware of the pain it brought. Although he normally stayed close to his family, he did all he could to keep Harry company and cheer him up in those sad days after Lucille's departure.

ALF ROBERTS' SENSE OF DUTY

'I have a quiet life. I like the odd drink. Phyllis enjoys her bingo. We seldom see each other.'

After a brief spell in the Cheshires at the end of the war, Alf Roberts went back to the GPO on Demob.

A tragic car accident in 1949 resulted in the death of Alf Roberts' older brother Malcolm, and a heart-rending dilemma for the 23-year-old Alf. Malcolm and his wife Phyllis were well off in every sense of the word. Phyllis Plant came from a family with money and when she married Malcolm, an accounts clerk at the GPO, in 1946, her father settled quite a tidy sum on the newlyweds. They used the money to buy, outright, their house in Omdurman Street, Weatherfield.

It was not a marriage blessed with great passion, excitement or children but Malcolm and Phyllis got on with their sober lives comfortably and cheerfully as the post-war world tried to cope with hardships, shortages and political unrest.

Alf, who had recently followed his brother into employment with the GPO, was a frequent visitor to their home and often called to assist Malcolm in the odd jobs that Malcolm found so difficult. Alf's wartime experiences in the 7th Cheshires, where he had served out his time between May 1945 and demob by becoming the unit maintenance man, had left him with a good knowledge of all things mechanical — unlike Malcolm.

A special 'treat' for Alf was Sunday evenings when Phyllis invited him and her two sisters, Laura and Maude, to her musical evening around the Roberts' splendid HMV radiogram. They listened first to Albert Sandler and the Palm Court Orchestra and then heard selections from Phyllis' Gilbert and Sullivan collection and other gems of light opera she'd accumulated in her formative years.

After Alf attended his first evening he was all for making excuses to avoid further experiences, but his father Sydney and mother Eileen urged, if not ordered, him to attend. Laura and Maude Plant were very eligible young ladies. Alf, Sydney kept telling him, could do a lot worse than either of those young women.

Reluctantly, Alf dressed up each Sunday and joined the little group around the HMV. Half oranges and chocolates were passed round at the interval, while Phyllis made tea, and Alf attempted conversation with his two sisters-in-law. Neither was a beauty but Alf settled on Laura and asked her out to see a play at the Alhambra theatre the next Saturday.

Sadly it was a date Alf was unable to keep as he spent that Saturday night in hospital where he had been taken after an accident in his brother's new Lanchester car had left Alf with a broken arm and Malcolm dead. When news of Malcolm's death was brought to Alf's bedside by his mother and father he quickly took responsibility for the accident. He had been driving when the car had swerved into the path of a brick lorry to avoid a child who had run out into the road.

Malcolm had been on the impact side and received serious head injuries as the car crashed into the front end of the massive, weighty vehicle. Alf went over in his mind all the things he might have done to avoid the accident. But, in the end, he'd made a split-second decision to save the child and Malcolm had died.

Back in Omdurman Street, Phyllis was distraught and Alf became a frequent caller, taking over in almost every way from his late brother. It was Sydney Roberts who first suggested that Alf could do a lot worse than to step completely into his brother's shoes and marry his widow. Poor Alf was ridden with guilt and felt so sorry for Phyllis, but he did not love her.

One year after Malcolm's death, Alf and Phyllis were married and, as they posed for the wedding photographs, no one would have suspected that Alf's cheerful smile disguised a sad man who was just performing a necessary task. While all around forecast a rosy future for the happy couple, united in grief and then in love, Alf saw his future as a sacrifice for life — but what else could he do? It was his duty.

Alf's fellow GPO worker, Frank Barlow, arrived home late after military service in Iraq which had made his worried wife Ida think he might have been killed in action. It was only during the VE Day celebrations, that Ida was told of his imminent return, and that he had been kept back for special duties. She was delighted that her life alone had ended and to be able to tell her two young sons, Kenneth and David, that their father would soon be back.

Kenneth, dressed in his make-shift soldier's uniform as part of the VE Day carnival float, could barely contain his excitement at the prospect of seeing the father he barely remembered. He had last seen Frank Barlow on his embarkation leave in 1941.

≋ KENNETH BARLOW MAKES IT ≋

'The people in my street are all the same: happily starved of culture, lazy minded and politically ignorant. They're more concerned with their local pub than they are with world affairs.'

Frank Barlow and his son Kenneth could never see eye to eye over anything. Working-class Frank, a GPO employee, couldn't understand why his elder son had wanted to go to University to study to become a teacher. For his part, Kenneth equally resented Frank's insistence that he should conduct his life in the same style as Frank and Frank's father before him.

When Ken had passed his eleven-plus examination in 1950 and dashed home with the news, Ida, his mother, was delighted; Kenneth was the apple of her eye and to see him succeed where others had failed, confirmed her faith in her son's ability.

After a brief perusal of the enrolment papers for grammar school, Frank dismissed them as rubbish and told Ken that money was not going to be wasted on uniforms, gym kit or any of the basic requirements of Weatherfield Grammar, so that his son could become a learned snob.

The Barlows in happier days when David, his Dad's favourite, was working at an engineering works and Kenneth, his mum's pride and joy, was at university.

Young David Barlow hardly knew his father in his early years, as Frank served abroad during the war and did not arrive home until well after Demob.

While Kenneth protested angrily and Ida reasoned, Frank remained adamant — Kenneth was going to Bessie Street Seniors like other Coronation Street residents — Billy Walker, Christine Hardman and Linda Tanner.

At Bessie Street, Ken turned his resentment against his father into a determination to do well. While his contemporaries concentrated their efforts on matters away from school, he read and studied hard so that with extra tuition from school teacher Ada Hayes, the sister of Esther Hayes, the Barlow's family friend from Number 5, he was able to sit his GCE examinations privately and gain nine 'O' Levels.

All of this happened without Frank's consent or knowledge. Ida paid for Kenneth's private tuition herself, out of the money she earned from cleaning and washing up at the Imperial Hotel, in Manchester. At 15 Kenneth left Bessie Street, but with his nine 'O' Levels was able to gain a position at the sixth form at Weatherfield Grammar. Frank, in spite of his earlier misgivings, was quite pleased to have a successful son to talk about at the post office and in the Rovers where Billy Walker's *lack* of achievement was the usual topic behind his mother's back.

Kenneth's intelligence had made him a bit of an outsider at Bessie Street, where Billy Walker was the typical role model. Now, at the grammar school, the situation worked in reverse and he found himself again an outsider for totally different reasons. His manners and personal cleanliness were questioned by the school wags, solely because he came from Bessie Street School and lived in down-at-heel Coronation Street.

Never one to be put down and fully aware he was being put on because he came from Bessie Street, Kenneth worked hard and quite easily obtained the two 'A' Levels necessary to take up a place at Manchester University.

Kenneth had proved his point to both Frank and his doubting friends at the grammar school. The self-confident, outspoken young man who commenced his studies at the university had come a long way from the shy, retiring youngster who had first sat down at a battered desk at Bessie Street School.

Vera Sharples, Ena's daughter, married Bob Lomax and escaped from the Mission of Glad Tidings to a semi-detached across town.

The dawn of the Fifties was overshadowed by more talk of war. Everyone felt twice was enough, but when the name of Korea, far away in Asia, suddenly clogged the airwaves and filled the front pages of the newspapers, the grim spectre of loss and separation once more threatened the country.

Now it was the boys doing National Service who were to take up the cause and sadly and apprehensively mothers watched their young sons, barely out of school, set off in uniform for a strange land on the other side of the world. This time, the losses were not so severe, but just as devastating to the families who lost their loved ones. Coronation Street suffered no victims, but from Nightingale Street, Geoffrey Cook departed with the Gloucesters, never to return. And from Kitchener Street, 18-year-old John 'Spider' Webb was awarded the Military Medal for conspicuous gallantry under fire while holding a position outside the capital city of Seoul. He returned in a wheelchair and was never to walk again.

The new Queen was crowned on 2 June 1953 and Coronation Street, like all the other streets in Weatherfield celebrated with a musical extravaganza put on by Leonard Swindley at the Mission of Glad Tidings. One of the stars of the pageant was young Lucille Hewitt who played handmaiden to landlady Annie Walker's Queen Victoria and sang *There's a Golden Coach* beautifully, to the rapturous applause of the audience and a special hug from her proud father afterwards.

Wedding bells were not heard so often during this era when everyone was just getting back to normal life, but notable weddings included Albert Tatlock's daughter Beattie from Number 1 Coronation Street, who married Norman Pearson in 1953, and Ena Sharple's daughter Vera who married Bob Lomax from Mawdsley Street in 1946 — both couples moved to vacant, semi-detached houses situated on the other side of town.

One newly married couple that moved in to Coronation Street was Ted Gibson and Amy Foster who married at St Mary's Church in 1950 and moved into Number 9. Ted was a clerk at Dave Smith's betting shop but never had a flutter except on the pools. Next-door neighbour Linda Tanner from Number 11 married her Polish boyfriend Ivan Cheveski in 1958 and was given away by her uncle Arthur. Linda had met Ivan at an Anglo-Polish dance at Manchester's Ritz Ballroom. Taking after her mother, the infamous Elsie Tanner, Linda was, at the time, engaged to an American GI. However, as soon as she saw muscular Ivan she ditched Paul and set her heart on a white wedding. They set up home in Warrington. A surprise wedding took place in Weatherfield in 1949 when schoolteacher Ada Hayes from Number 5 suddenly married Matt Harvey at the age of 39.

In the middle of the 1950s, the corner shop in Coronation Street was just beginning to recover from the drastic effects of food rationing, which had continued well beyond the end of the war. Suddenly, everything was available and with increased advertising in the plentiful women's magazines, the cinema (by now, playing to massive audiences) and occasionally from TV advertising, a whole

Albert Tatlock's daughter Beattie married Norman Pearson on 10 May 1953. Her visits to her parents' home became less frequent after her mother, Bessie's death in August 1959.

new world of pre-packaged goods arrived.

Elsie Foyle, who ran the shop, was widowed on VE Day and had then married Les Lappin but he himself died in 1952. She now found she had to keep up with the times and stock her shelves with a variety of goods from all parts of the world.

Unaffected by the modern trend was the elite grocery run by George Hardman in Rosamund Street. Hardman's represented tradition and quality and was seldom frequented by the relatively hard-up residents of Coronation Street. Sadly for Hardman's, this was soon all to change.

After her father's death, Christine Hardman quickly readjusted her life and learned to live with her mother, reminiscing about what had been.

≈ CHRISTINE COMES BACK TO THE STREET ≈

'Girls like me are stuck. Stuck 'ere in this glory hole. This midden of a street where there's no hope for owt different.'

George Hardman's sudden death in June 1955, at fifty years old, was one of the saddest moments of Christine Hardman's life. Much grief lay in the future for her, but the beginning of 1955 had seen her blissfully happy.

She was sixteen years old and already establishing herself as her father's most able assistant in his grocer's shop in the nice part of Rosamund Street. George Hardman had left his secure job in a bank to buy the grocery shop in 1949. It proved so successful that the following year the family moved from Coronation Street to a smart, semi-detached house in Abingdon Road.

Hardman's offered a new dimension of quality and service to people from the comfortable Oakhill area of Weatherfield. Not only did they have the finest cheese, tea and coffee but visitors were able to wait in the pleasant surroundings while George Hardman or the efficient Mrs Coker patted their butter into shape.

They even had their own delivery van in its claret and primrose livery, which carried their goods to their well-off customers in the area. Behind the scenes, young Christine, two years out of Bessie Street School, thrived as she worked at the busy grocer's shop.

Hilda Coker, George's able assistant, was nearing retirement after almost fifty years in the establishment she'd worked at since she left school and she made sure that Christine was trained well as her successor.

Christine was a bright, attractive young girl and the long-established customers developed an easy rapport with her based on her reliability and friendliness. She had changed considerably since she first reported for work when she left Bessie Street School. Then, she had been quiet and withdrawn and had her mind set on furthering her education, like Kenneth Barlow.

Both George and, more importantly May, who ruled the Hardman family from their home in Abingdon Road, wanted Christine in the family

May Hardman had got used to money, success and living in Oakhill when, owing to changed circumstances, she was forced to return to her roots in Coronation Street.

business for different reasons. May saw Christine eventually taking over the business so that she and George could enjoy their retirement in a place like Grange or Southport. George was happy to have someone he could trust in the business and someone whom he could pay less than the going rate for the job.

February 1955 brought about the end of everyone's dreams when George Hardman collapsed in the small back office of the shop during a heated telephone conversation with the biscuit suppliers. He died a short time later from a massive heart attack.

The heated conversation turned out to have been one of many such conversations privately conducted in the back office between George and a string of his suppliers. The correspondence discovered locked away in that office revealed that insolvency was closing in on Hardman's and that in many cases suppliers had stopped sending any more goods because of non-payment.

The receivers moved in, and with the shop and its contents sold, Hilda Coker was paid a small part of her hard-earned retirement pension and

Christine given an envelope with four pounds ten and sixpence for her last week's work. The receiver's eye then turned to their beloved property in Abingdon Road.

May Hardman, proud to the end, had to suffer the indignity of handing over the keys of her hard-earned house to the bailiff and waving goodbye to the three years it had taken to turn it into a home.

Early the next morning, while the neighbours were still in their beds, May and Christine walked down Abingdon Road for the last time. Fortunately, they had kept up their links with their old neighbours in Coronation Street where they had lived at Number 13 for 22 years before success had taken them to the smarter part of town.

Elsie Lappin at the corner shop, who had been their next-door neighbour in Coronation Street for many years, made enquiries about their old house next door, still empty, and got the landlord's agreement for the Hardmans to move back. It was a sad homecoming. Grateful as she was to Elsie Lappin, somehow, it was almost with resentment that May returned to take up residence next to a scruffy little corner shop which she now could barely afford to patronise.

Gone was the driving, ambitious May Hardman of the early years. In her place was a vague, distant and unfriendly widow who kept herself to herself and tried to make young Christine do the same.

For her part, Christine did not take things so badly. She had grown up in the street and had not had time at Abingdon Road to become accustomed to a better way of life. She soon found a job at Elliston's raincoat factory and gradually, as her mother became more depressed, took over the rudder as head of the family.

With May's constant demands on her time, her social life was drastically curtailed, but she was young, pretty and out of debt. Things could only get better now, she consoled herself, and there was one big advantage to being back in Coronation Street — Ken Barlow would soon be back from Manchester University.

After the war, Dot Greenhalgh set up home at 18 Victoria Street. Her only child, Samantha, died of TB aged 13 months.

The late 1950s saw many changes in Weatherfield. The trams which had ran along Rosamund Street for over 50 years were replaced with diesel buses. The LMS railway, which had proudly borne its liveried rolling stock over the viaduct since the last century, gave way to British Rail, and all the main roads underwent major resurfacing work as the cobbles were removed and replaced with tarmac.

The new council houses on the Hammond Road Estate created a first in Weatherfield when they were built with the luxury of an inside toilet and nearby bathroom, and over in Victoria Street people enjoyed living in the less constricting semi-detached houses, which were built on the site of the network of small, scruffy streets demolished in 1958.

⚘ BLANCHE FINALLY LEAVES THE PUB ⚘

'I'm what they call in the Hollywood films a dangerous woman.
Barbara Stanwyck could do a picture about me.'

Blanche Hunt had reason to be pleased with life in July 1955 when her daughter Deirdre was born. Her husband Donald was a bank manager, she had a semi-detached house (on a bank-subsidized mortgage) in Victoria Street and, after two years of marriage she now had a bright, pretty young daughter.

At the age of four, Deirdre Hunt was less upset at the loss of her father than at the prospect of having to wear spectacles.

113

As a single girl and as a widow, Blanche Hunt kept her appearance up to date and was never without a male companion. However as a wife she remained completely faithful.

After a lifetime of association with the licensed trade — she'd been born over a pub in Pear Street — she seemed at last to have arrived at the middle-class position her mother, Iris, a barmaid at the Stevedore's Arms, had forecast for her.

Her father had died during the Depression, leaving Iris to bring up Blanche in a succession of small rooms over various public houses in the area. Iris's training as a dressmaker was discarded with the necessity of keeping a roof over the heads of herself and her daughter.

At her mother's insistence, Blanche was apprenticed as a corset maker at La Belle Foundations, but her other wish that she should improve herself by associations outside the licensed trade was made more difficult by World War Two and the comings and goings it brought about.

Life at La Belle was not particularly exciting for a girl of seventeen, with all the young men at war, and only her immature fellow apprentices for company. Things were different back at the Stevedore's, a dockside tavern frequented by sailors, servicemen in transit, and a small clientele of locally based US servicemen with money to spend on a good time. Iris looked on, shocked at her daughter's 'wanton' behaviour as she joked, laughed and had a good time with the constantly changing revellers.

Young Blanche had to content herself with just one night off each week, which she usually spent at a dance hall. On one occasion, at the Ritz Ballroom, she met up with a cocky Londoner, Dave Smith, and enjoyed her first relationship.

Dave was a spiv, but he gave Blanche a good time until she ditched him for an impressive US Master Sergeant who snatched her from under Dave's nose at the Tower Ballroom, Blackpool.

The war ended and Master Sergeant Hirsch went back to Brooklyn. Iris died in 1947 and Blanche quit La Belle, after five years, to take up a barmaid's job for three pounds ten shillings a week.

It was when she was working at the Flying Horse in Jubilee Terrace that she met Donald Hunt whose bank was close by, and he would often come in at lunchtime for a sandwich. They married in 1953 and moved into a large Victorian house with a garden, in Victoria Street. Two years later Deirdre was born. At last, Blanche was out from behind the bar and she often thought to herself how proud Iris would have been of her.

Deirdre had a happy home to grow up in, but early in 1960 Donald died at the young age of 42. At four, the impact of his death was far less harrowing for young Deirdre than the prospect of wearing the glasses that had just been prescribed to prevent her frequent headaches. Equally disturbing to her was the dentist's report that recommended a brace for her teeth.

Poor Blanche had to bear the devastating loss of her husband and the hostility of her young daughter all at the same time. As they left for the funeral and Blanche put on the sad little girl's glasses, she was obliged to make one concession. Deirdre had to wear the glasses, but she could do without the brace for her teeth.

And so the wind of change had truly blown through Coronation Street. The heroes had returned to better times. To the older residents like Ena Sharples and Albert Tatlock the world had gone mad and would never be the same again.

In 1947 the *Weatherfield Gazette* announced the death of Mrs Mabel Hardcastle (née Grimshaw) from Oakhill. Few were aware that, in her passing, Weatherfield had lost one of its prime architects and one in whose heart the welfare of Weatherfield had always been uppermost.

To some of the returning heroes, such as the well-set-up Harry Hewitt and Frank Barlow, the future was bright and promised much more.

To Ken Barlow, Christine Hardman and Billy Walker, the children of the war, a whole new set of standards and opportunities lay ahead. Weatherfield was ready to enter the Swinging Sixties.

Leonard Swindley as a spiv in a performance of Edgar Wallace's On The Spot *at the Mission of Glad Tidings.*

CHAPTER 8

1960-1968:
THE SWINGING SIXTIES

Keeping watch on the morals of Mawdsley and Coronation Streets — Martha and Ena.

BULLDOZERS ANNOUNCED THE new decade in Weatherfield. They arrived by the dozen, smashing through the tight-knit communities of people who were then condemned to live in 'streets in the sky'. Previously unknown tower blocks sprung up on the east of town, built on the bomb sites left over from the Blitz. They were named after famous British leaders in an attempt to instill some patriotic feelings in their reluctant occupants. Churchill House, Nelson House and Atlee House towered over the closely built terraces still standing on Irlam Road, but the shadow of the bulldozers loomed ever closer.

For the residents of Coronation Street the threat of demolition was ever present. Ena Sharples was sent to Coventry by all her neighbours after misreading a Town Hall notice that announced the demolition of Coronation Terrace. Four months previously the residents had huddled together in the Mission hall, reminiscing about the war years, as a gas leak was made safe in Mawdsley Street. Three years later, in 1964, the residents had to evacuate to the Mission basement where Ena once again donned her famous ARP helmet. An unexploded bomb had been unearthed in the back yard at Number 1 and the army was called in to defuse it. The incident was not an isolated one, Weatherfield still suffered from the after-effects of the war and twelve unexploded bombs were discovered in the 20 years following the blitz. Many houses in the area had been made unsafe by the bombings and were either pulled down or fell down prematurely.

The disused colliery shafts running under the heart of Weatherfield caused subsidence and settlement problems in many of the streets. In the case of Number 7 Coronation Street, movements in the foundations of the house caused the bay window support to move badly and the whole front of the house fell in. Fortunately its former occupant, Harry Hewitt and his new wife Concepta had left the area to live in Ireland so no one was hurt during the collapse. Instead of rebuilding the front wall, the landlord, Mr Wormold, made the decision to demolish the house. In his view the whole area ought to be included in the slum clearance plans.

One feature of pre-war Weatherfield was drastically altered in May 1967. The railway viaduct, constructed in the 1830s by the Great Northern Railway company, had been in a very bad state of repair since the end of the war. Bombing and subsidence had caused

Elsie Tanner supported her children with no help from her absent husband, Arnold. When Dennis fell in with the wrong crowd, he was led into petty thieving, resulting in a six-month spell in Borstal.

Local boy Jerry Booth bought Number 13 Coronation Street in 1963. He had to give up the house after falling behind with mortgage repayments.

enough movement to its structure to force the railway company to redirect passenger trains onto another route. However, goods trains still used the viaduct as a route to Manchester. It was one of these trains that crashed through the dilapidated viaduct on 8 May 1967. The wagons crashed down and smashed into some houses on Viaduct Street, killing Mr and Mrs Henderson at Number 23. The guard's wagon landed in Coronation Street, bringing all the viaduct down with it and totally burying the archway to Jubilee Terrace with bricks, rubble and twisted metal. Hair stylist Sonia Peters was killed instantly as she had been standing under the archway talking to Ena Sharples. Miraculously Ena Sharples was dragged from the wreckage alive, with only cuts and bruises to show for her ordeal. After the area had been cleared, the viaduct was rebuilt to its original state, but no trains were ever allowed to travel along it again.

Not all of Coronation Street's residents spent the early Sixties with

Frank Barlow left Coronation Street in May 1964, three years after his wife's tragic death under the wheels of a Corporation bus. Frank used a £5000 win on the Premium Bonds to move to leafy Cheshire.

problems. Frank Barlow won £5,000 on the Premium Bonds and used the money to retire to Cheshire. His wife Ida had died at the young age of 45, run over by a bus on Rosamund Street, and their younger son David had left the area to follow a career as a professional footballer. The residents followed his progress in the national newspapers and he had become a hero in his home town. The Gibsons also left the area; Ted had won the vast sum of £20,000 in November 1960. It only took him two days to decide what to do with the money and the couple set off on a round-the-world cruise before settling down to live in Dorset.

Mrs Florrie Lindley, who took over the corner shop on Coronation Street when Elsie Lappin retired, won £500 on the Premium Bonds and used most of the money to buy a new wardrobe. Following the current trends she transformed the tiny grocery shop into a sub post office, complete with an inside telephone kiosk. Private telephones were now becoming quite popular in the local houses, although the pubs still provided a pay-phone service.

Ena Sharples inherited Number 11 Coronation Street in 1965 when a member of the Mission congregation who had always enjoyed her harmonium playing left her the house in her will.

Ena at first contemplated evicting tenant Elsie Tanner, but after many rows with her, she decided the money would be more helpful and sold the property to Edward Wormold, the original landlord, for £300. House prices rose dramatically in Weatherfield in the early Sixties. At the end of 1960 the residents of Coronation Street were offered the chance to buy their homes for £200 — no tenant took the offer up as no one thought they would be good investments. Eight years later Len Fairclough, the local builder, bought Number 9 for £1,000.

⚞ LEN FAIRCLOUGH — UNLUCKY IN LOVE ⚟

'This is you an' me Elsie: backstreets, dirty canals and factory hooters. We belong 'ere and always will.'

The date 22 November 1963 was one Len Fairclough was to remember all his life. He was not alone. Across the Atlantic, in Dallas, Texas, the popular American president, John F. Kennedy, was assassinated as he drove to a political rally. While the world's attention was held by the disastrous events in America, in Weatherfield Len sat in his Mawdsley Street house trying to work out where he'd gone wrong. For as well as being the day John Kennedy died, 22 November was also the day Elsie Tanner had refused to marry him.

Since his wife Nellie had left home a year previously, taking their 12-year-old son Stanley with her, Len had relied heavily on Elsie. He had told her that marrying Nellie had been a mistake; they had been far too young and too influenced by the romantic relationships they had seen on the cinema screen. If only Elsie had gone out with him instead that night she had met Arnold Tanner at a party, life could have been so different.

Elsie had turned down his marriage proposal saying that they were better staying as friends and she didn't want to risk losing that special relationship. Besides, she was as much a failure at marriage as he was.

The talk in the Rovers Return was dominated by Kennedy's death and what would happen to his widow. Shocked by the day's events, the customers could only speculate as to what effect the death would have worldwide. Len refused to be drawn into conversation by his usual drinking partners and sat alone remembering Nellie's last words to him: 'You're an idle pig. You ruin everything you touch; you've ruined my life, my happiness, our marriage. You're useless. Go to your tart. Go to Elsie flamin' Tanner. See if she'll 'ave you. If she's any sense she'll spit in yer eye, like I should 'ave done years ago.' In some ways Nellie had been right all along.

Leonard Franklin Fairclough had married Nellie Briggs on 12 July 1949 at the Mission of Glad Tidings. The marriage ended when Nellie, fed up of living with a boozy, violent, chauvinistic husband, ran off with the insurance man.

With the Government encouraging people to branch out in private enterprise, the last of the Weatherfield mills closed their doors and smaller factories took over as the main employers. Businesses set up after the war, providing employment for the women refusing to stay at home, began to find it hard to recruit willing employees. Children were encouraged to stay on at school, to work for higher qualifications and to attend colleges to give them a choice of career. Granston Technical College opened its doors in 1962. It served as a college of further education as well as taking apprentices for day-release courses. Encouraged to better themselves with examinations, certificates and diplomas, the young people traditionally destined for mill work now sought out the best career openings for themselves. As well as the technical college, a secretarial college and a hair stylists' school opened on Rosamund Street.

Florrie Lindley, like all small shopkeepers, struggled to keep trading as new supermarkets opened up all over the town. With their longer hours and variety of stock, they attracted customers who now found their local shops inadequate. However, a large number of shoppers disliked the lack of personal contact they were accustomed to. Ena Sharples persuaded her neighbours to boycott the new Summit Supermarket in Victoria Street when the manager had asked her to move on and stop gossiping in the aisles. Sylvia Snape, who ran a small café on Rosamund Street, found the trade from housewives dying off as, using the new bus system, they were encouraged to shop in Manchester. She sold up whilst Leonard Swindley found himself caught up in the changes that were affecting all shops.

Florrie Lindley posed as a widow for the benefit of her customers. In reality she was estranged from her engineer husband, Norman, who worked in India.

VOTE FOR SWINDLEY

'Life is changing all around. The little man in the street is tired of being trodden on. Today it is a sad but true case of unite or go under. Swindleys do not go under.'

Since the death of his father Thomas in 1958, Leonard Swindley had tried his best to uphold and run the family drapers shop on Rosamund Street. Established in 1902 by his grandfather, William Swindley, the shop had been a thriving business. At its prime in 1920 it had a staff of six and a young lad who was paid to hold the horses still as their well-off owners climbed down from carriages to enter the emporium.

Those days, Leonard often mused, were sadly over. No one seemed to want to work in small shops any more and the demand for wing-collar studs and ladies' hat pins was no longer enough to make the shop a profitable business. The stock room was filled with dusty boxes containing goods that people would laugh at if they were placed on display.

Leonard Swindley had tried to change with the times. He had brought in what he considered to be new lines, but these items were more expensive to stock and never seemed to sell as well as they should. After the bank manager had refused him a much-needed loan, Leonard had taken the only option open to him — to sell out to someone else. Greek tycoon, Niklos Papagopolous, eagerly bought the business and good will (what little remained) and the shop was transformed into the sixth retail outlet in his chain of stores and was renamed: 'Gamma Garments'.

Much to his relief, Leonard still carried responsibility for the shop as its manager. Taking his instructions straight from Papagopolous, he stocked the shop's windows with the latest fashions, while keeping the old goods in the stock room for the few customers who had remained faithful to him.

It was as a small trader that Leonard stood for the local Council elections in 1962. As a committee member of the Progressive Property Owners (and Small Traders) Party, he was nominated to stand for the elections as a polite gesture. Although some of his colleagues tried to hide their concern, Leonard was aware that no one had any faith in him as a figure head. He had planned to stand down in favour of the more dynamic butcher, William Piggott, but he had failed to turn up for the election meeting and Swindley was forced to stand.

Improved street lighting was the PPOP's main local concern and Leonard surprised members of the party by drumming up considerable support as he included in his manifesto the problems of traffic travelling along the main street. Rallying for votes, Leonard took over the Mission of Glad Tidings for a debating evening. As luck would have it, the Mission boiler chose that particular evening to explode and the meeting ended in chaos. After weeks of hard campaigning, Leonard was disappointed when he lost the election by 405 votes to Labour's Joe Armstrong, who received 1,642 votes.

Papagopolous had been impressed by the way Leonard had organized his campaign and told him, in his forthright manner, that previously he had hardly rated him as managerial material. The election campaign, however, had opened his eyes. Leonard decided to take this as a compliment and readily agreed when his boss offered him the job of area manager at Gamma Garments. Unleashed from the drab counter where he had worked all his life, Leonard began to enjoy a new freedom that he realized he had always yearned for.

One thing about Leonard still remained the same however: he constantly reminded himself that he was still a Swindley and to a Swindley the customer was *always* right, come what may.

An election poster from Leonard Swindley's campaign for the 1962 Council elections.

Niklos Papagopolous' Manchester chainstore, Gamma Garments, came to Weatherfield in 1962 when he opened his sixth store in Rosamund Street.

◁ EMILY NUGENT — ▷
SPINSTER OF THIS PARISH

*'I'm your favourite spinster. A bit too precise ... too tidy. Getting
a little too particular, a bit querulous. Anxious to be friendly,
but terribly afraid of being — rebuffed. Always available.
Always **there**. But always in the background.'*

For 25 years, Miss Irene Pemberton had been Leonard Swindley's loyal and trusted assistant at his haberdashery emporium on Rosamund Street. For every one of those long years she had secretly nurtured the hope that one day he might look upon her as more than just an employee. The longed-for day had never come, but she had managed to comfort herself with the knowledge that no other woman had any contact with the man she so worshipped and adored. And so it was on the day that Emily Nugent brought her stock of baby linen into the shop in order to merge their businesses, that Irene Pemberton decided to walk out. She knew the moment she set eyes on the timid Emily that she was exactly the sort of helpless female who would finally make a husband of Leonard Swindley. It was of no surprise to her when, three years later, she read of the couple's engagement in the *Gazette*.

Born in Harrogate, the daughter of retired Sergeant Major James Nugent, Emily sacrificed most of her youth helping to bring up her younger sisters and brother. She moved to Weatherfield in 1954 to escape her domineering father.

It had taken those three years for Emily Nugent also to realize that she was going to have to wait forever if she wanted Leonard Swindley to see her as anything but a shop assistant and confidante. Taking advantage of Leap Year 1964, it was she who proposed to the surprised and reluctant lay preacher. At first, the idea had not appealed to Swindley; he did not love Emily, but slowly the advantages became clear and he realized he would be a fool to allow a free housekeeper and excellent cook to slip through his fingers.

As both the bride and groom served on the committee at the Mission circuit, it seemed appropriate that they should marry at the Mission of Glad Tidings. It was as the groom and the congregation were waiting for her triumphant appearance that Emily realized she could not marry Leonard. She saw that their marriage would only be based on companionship, and not love, and felt it would be a mockery of all she believed in. Leonard, of course, understood perfectly and their working relationship was in no way spoilt. Emily, however, found that she no longer accepted everything her boss said as being correct and she began to explore her own, excellent, business sense.

When Leonard Swindley left Weatherfield in

1965 it was a natural progression for Emily to take control of the shop. For three years the premises had been part of a chain store, Gamma Garments, owned by Greek businessman, Niklos Papagopolous. Emily Nugent enjoyed running the shop, but when the chance came up of a position working in Majorca she jumped at it. The job was that of gift shop manageress and the prospect of living in the romantic Mediterranean was enormously appealing. But poor Emily's dreams were ruined when she found herself obliged to care for her ailing father. Persuaded by her uncaring sisters, she had to exchange all thoughts of Majorca for Harrogate, and spent a year there at the beck and call of her father until she was exhausted.

It was with a great deal of excitement that Emily returned to Weatherfield and Gamma Garments in 1967. Papagopolous gave her a free hand and she updated the store into a fashion boutique. Lucille Hewitt joined her to help her sell the new, popular mini skirts while Dennis Tanner took care of the 'Gamma Man'. Emily gave herself a totally new image and caught up with the latest mode of speech — everything became 'fab' and 'swinging'. She even started to date Brian Thomas, an old school friend of Lucille's, who was 17 years her junior. She introduced him to a girl of his own age. Emily put a stop to their liaisons when Brian became too intense. Emily's opinion was sought on dress sense and fashion and her work at the Mission continued to fill her evenings.

Although she was kept very busy, as she neared her fortieth birthday in 1967, Emily felt that her dream of a husband and home would never come to fruition. She decided to broaden her horizons and shocked her neighbours by placing a personal ad in the local paper. Expressing her interest in unusual hobbies, it attracted only one interested party, a weight lifter. Emily then decided to join a marriage bureau. Unfortunately her two potential suitors turned out to be thoroughly unsuitable — one was a farmer who was seeking a partner to share his love of the outdoor life, the other was a weak-willed individual trying to escape from a domineering sister.

Two events in 1968 affected Emily's working and private life. First Papagopolous declared himself bankrupt in the summer; Emily was given no warning and was very bitter at losing her job. She retaliated by using the company phone for a lengthy chat with her friend working in Majorca. It was during this period of adjustment that Miklos Zadic entered Emily's life. He was a Hungarian teacher who had fled his native country after the 1956 uprising. He was employed in England as a demolition expert and his handsome, strong, masculine looks caused a great stir among the women folk. It was quiet, predictable Emily, however, in whom he showed a great interest. She prepared elaborate picnics to share with him on the building sites where he worked, and he introduced her to the benefits of communism, arousing a passion in her that she hardly knew existed.

To everyone's surprise — not least her own — Emily Nugent gave up her flat and followed Miklos to Scotland where they spent a week of intense passion together. When she returned, alone, Emily told Valerie Barlow that, for once in her life, she had no regrets about what had happened.

Sober, conservative Emily missed out on much of the spirit of the 1960s, unlike her more freewheeling neighbours such as Dot Greenhalgh and Lucille Hewitt.

Miklos Zadic had fled Hungary during the 1956 uprising. A talented teacher, he was forced to find employment as a demolition worker.

With a £200 deposit and a mortgage for £350, lorry driver Stan Ogden bought Number 13 Coronation Street in June 1964. His charlady wife Hilda soon found work at the Rovers Return, where their daughter Irma served as a barmaid.

With the new variety of places to work came a more affluent lifestyle as the mill owners' hold on wages was broken. Older members of society were shocked by the way the younger generation spent their earnings. Harry Hewitt saved the bulk of his wages as a bus inspector to buy a 1957 convertible, while young Kenneth Barlow celebrated obtaining his Bachelor of Arts degree by buying himself a scooter. Suddenly holidays abroad were accessible to many working people and the traditional day trip to Blackpool became a thing of the past as people were encouraged to save for a holiday in Europe. Even Ena Sharples overcame her fear of flying to spend three months visiting her brother Tom in America. Television sets became a priority in most Weatherfield homes, more so than fridges or inside toilets.

Stan and Hilda Ogden moved into Number 13 Coronation Street in June 1964 from Chapel Street when Stan was forced to give up driving lorries and needed a new home for all the family. Two of their children, Sylvia and Tony, had been taken into care when Hilda had been unable to cope with them on her own. Their 19-year-old daughter Irma met football star David Barlow on one of his rare visits to the street. He was amused when she didn't know who he was, even though that week's *Gazette* carried his photograph on the front page. They married a year later, in December 1965. Only a few weeks after their marriage a leg injury forced David to give up professional football and they decided to take over the corner shop. They bought the business for £1750 and the stock for £200 from Lionel Petty who had run the shop-come-post office for just over a year.

Kenneth Barlow also got married. After graduating from Man-

Nancy Leathers proudly looked on as her grandson Kenneth married Valerie Tatlock at St Mary's Church on 4 August 1962.

chester University, he settled into a teaching post at Bessie Street School where he himself had been a pupil. He married the girl next door, Albert Tatlock's niece Valerie, in 1962. Valerie opened a hair salon in the front parlour of their new home, Number 9 Coronation Street, after they bought it for £565. Three years later Valerie gave birth to twins, Susan and Peter.

Elsie and Arnold Tanner were finally divorced in 1961, although their marriage had really finished in 1945. Arnold married again immediately, his bride was Norah Dawson who ran a toffee shop in Nelson Street. Elsie also embarked on marriage again, her groom was her old love, Master Sgt Steve Tanner of the US Army, the same man she had fallen so madly in love with twenty years ago. Steve had returned to Burtonwood after serving in France. Elsie was reluctant to meet him at first as she feared she had aged too much, but Steve hardly noticed any changes and said she was more beautiful than ever. Their swift and passionate romance led to a white wedding in Warrington and a subsequent, new life for Elsie in America. Many changes were happening in the street; many people were moving on.

American buddies Steve Tanner (left) and Gregg Flint (right) continually returned to Burtonwood. In September 1967 Steve finally married his wartime sweetheart, Elsie Tanner. It was Steve's second marriage; his first wife, Le Lan, had been killed in Vietnam when her village was bombed by mistake.

ESTHER HAYES, A VERY PRIVATE PERSON

'Whenever anyone in this street has a problem, they bring it to me. I suppose I ought to be flattered. But answering questions and 'elping folk doesn't take away any of the loneliness in life. I'm a very lonely person.'

Three tea chests full of memories. There could have been more, many more, but Esther had been very strict with herself. Now she was leaving Coronation Street she had no intention of dragging too many old ghosts with her. She was frightened of leaving the street where she had been born. She felt secure living among people she had known all her life. She knew their strengths and weaknesses, they knew hers. She knew all their pasts and they in turn knew all about her.

Esther Hayes was a private person and did not like the idea of neighbours knowing all about her. She had suffered pitying glances and knowing looks for nearly 20 years. The thought of starting life afresh where no one knew her had its own appeal. She wanted to leave her ghosts behind her at Number 5. She knew she shouldn't look upon all her memories as 'ghosts'; that only over-dramatized them in a way more typical of Ena Sharples than herself. Memories they were, and she was glad to leave them behind. Three particular incidents were behind these memories — three events that had shaped her life.

The first happened in 1942 when she had met Jack. Her father had died two years previously and her wages as a clerk, together with Ada's teaching money, allowed the family a certain amount of luxury despite World War

Esther Hayes had lived all her life at Number 5 Coronation Street. When she moved away in 1962 she willingly left behind unhappy memories.

Two, which cast a shadow over everyday life.

She had been feeding the ducks in North Cross Park. It was winter and frost was heavy on the ground. There was no ice on the pond, but Esther felt sorry for the birds, who always seemed desperate for food, and feeding them the crusts off her sandwiches was a daily event. On the day in question it was a particular frosty morning and she had slipped on the grass by the pond. The supports around the water had been taken away to be used in the war effort and for a moment Esther felt she would fall into the pond. A hand grabbed her as she fell over and supported her as she once again found her footing. She had thanked its owner, blushing slightly. He had smiled shyly and asked if he could join her in feeding the ducks. She found out that his name was John, but liked to be called Jack, and she agreed to let him walk her to work.

Walking alongside a boy in uniform made Esther feel confident for some unknown reason. Perhaps it was his natural good humour that affected her. When he had asked her for a lunch-time cup of tea, she had accepted.

Miss Esther Hayes' engagement to Mr John Brown of the 7th Cheshires, was announced the following summer in the *Weatherfield Gazette*. The wedding date was set for 7 October at the Mission of Glad Tidings where her father had been a lay preacher. The months leading up to the wedding were to be the happiest in Esther's life. Ada helped her make a beautiful dress with a silk underslip made from a parachute 'acquired' by brother Tom. Annie Walker laid on a two-tiered cake for the reception at the Rovers Return and Alice Hayes agreed to move out of the master bedroom in favour of the new man of the house. The household buzzed with excitement right up to two days before the wedding, when Jack's father called to say Jack had been killed, shot down in the plane that was bringing him home from abroad.

The second poignant incident was six years later as Esther watched her sister Ada marry Matt Harvey; she felt the neighbours watching her with pity in their eyes. 'It should have been me' was all she could think, although she tried desperately to push the thought to the back of her mind. Tom had left home a long time ago and now Ada was going to live in Australia. Biting her lip, suppressing bitterness she had never experienced before, Esther realized she was trapped — well and truly trapped. At home, in bed, her invalid mother waited impatiently for the return of her new nurse.

Alice Hayes was a bitter, ungrateful patient. Ignoring any effort Esther put into nursing her, she would continue to ask for news of her beloved son Tom. Esther often had to prevent herself from telling her mother the news that she had of Tom — he'd been imprisoned for four years for corruption. Instead, she would let the old lady hope that maybe the next day he would visit, or even write. Alice expected her youngest daughter to spend the rest of her life, if necessary, looking after her as she lay in bed with only a wireless for company.

Promotion was finally offered to Esther in early 1950, promotion that meant leaving Weatherfield for the South, and gave her the chance of more money and independence. A once-in-a-lifetime chance. The bang of her mother's stick on the floor above brought Esther back from her musings to the harsh reality of her situation.

The third incident that would always stay with Esther was when Alice died in her sleep in 1952. The relief was immense for Esther and she had to stop herself rushing into the street to announce the news. But then after only a morning, she began to feel guilty. Had she done all she could have for her mother? Had she respected her as she should have done? Could she have made her last years any happier? Despite the neighbours commenting on her saintly nature, Esther burdened herself with guilt and was haunted by the memory of a fragile old lady, whom she had grown to dislike so much.

Esther did not know if leaving Coronation Street would help her forget the past, but a new flat in fashionable Moor Lane awaited her. The neighbours had tried to hide their jealousy when she had announced her new position as head clerk at Masons, which included a flat with its own bathroom. Yes, she was glad to be going. Coronation Street held nothing but bad memories. Perhaps she wouldn't take any tea chests after all.

At 17 Esther had been madly in love with Jack Brown. She never recovered from his tragic death on the eve of their wedding in October 1942.

Miami Modes, the poor-man's Kendalls, offered five floors of fashion, furniture and household items. The department store sold affordable goods that were within reach of most of Weatherfield's residents.

The edition of the *Weatherfield Gazette* carrying the official photograph of the happy Tanner wedding group reported, on the same page, the death of Harry Hewitt. Harry had returned from Ireland to visit his daughter Lucille, who had remained in Weatherfield, lodging at the Rovers Return. As the visit coincided with neighbour Elsie's wedding, he and his wife Concepta had stayed on. It was after the reception that Harry had been killed, crushed to death under Len Fairclough's van while he attempted some repair work.

The new General Hospital, built on the site of the fire damaged Infirmary on Rosamund Street, prepared Harry's body for burial. Ena Sharples, who had laid out the local dead for over 40 years, made her own daughter her last client. Sadly, Vera Lomax had died in her mother's bed, from a brain tumour, in January 1967. Three years earlier Ena had been helped by Minnie Caldwell as she attended to their old friend Martha Longhurst's body. Martha had succumbed to a heart attack in the Snug of the Rovers Return on the eve of a longed-for Spanish holiday.

With his mother safely out of the country, Dennis Tanner made

Miami Modes

A new outfit for spring?

Come to MIAMI MODES for the very latest in fashionwear

Weatherfield
6521

use of the deserted family home to invite a group of 'flower people' to squat there. The hippie commune caused a public outcry as they lounged around Number 11, giving their views on love and sexual freedom to whoever passed by. Annie Walker, worried about the value of her property and her ward Lucille Hewitt's morals, reported Dennis to his landlord, Mr Wormold. The landlord had the commune forcibly evicted. They left a huge purple flower painted on the kitchen ceiling as their legacy. Sexual freedom was now advocated by many young women, but sometimes it had the pain of an earlier emotional loss.

⤳ BET'S LOSS OF FAITH IN MEN ⤝

'Hope keeps people like me going. You hope that one day there'll be someone who won't cheat or lie or pretend they care about you when all they really want is a willing woman. I've been kicked in the teeth often enough, so it doesn't really come as a surprise. But it doesn't stop hurting.'

26-year-old Bet Lynch from Clegg Street always made heads turn when she walked down Coronation Street. Behind her flirtatious smile lay emotional upset and heartache.

Bet Lynch took a plastic-welding job at Elliston's PVC factory on Coronation Street a week before her 26th birthday. When her birthday arrived she had already attracted the attention of foreman John Benjamin and was sharing his bed. While the other workers either admired her quick work or expressed their disapproval of her attitude to men, Bet felt that whatever she did was of no consequence, to John, the others or to herself. John was just the latest in a string of faceless men who had drifted in and out of her young life. Some had given her good memories, but most had left her with deep scars that would never be healed.

It was ten years ago, working in a grocer's shop and living at home with mother Mary, that she had fallen for Joe Mason, 12 years her senior. They had met at a party, where she had got drunk and he had been willing to take advantage of the situation. Nine months later their baby son was born; Joe had immediately disappeared when she told him about the baby, blaming Bet for not taking precautions. Her mother Mary marched her straight into the confessional at St Theresa's and listened in as the priest remonstrated strongly with her.

Bet begged forgiveness from God, but Mary took no notice and arranged for the child to be adopted as soon it was born. Bet pleaded to keep little Martin Andrew, but Mary threatened to throw her out if she did. The authorities came for Martin and drove away with him in a red van. Bet watched sadly from the window of the room that Mary had locked her in.

Since her mother had made no attempt to hide the fact that her daughter was pregnant, Bet found the whole of Clegg Street knew her situation. She had to endure all the women gossiping about her and their husbands and sons leering at her. She knew then, at the young age of 17, that she was branded for life as 'easy' and that no respectable man would ever look at her. She made up her mind at that point to make the most of what life had to offer and to get all she could from the men who were attracted to her. She might never get any love or emotional security from people like John Benjamin, but at least she knew that she could always be sure of a fatter pay packet than her fellow workers.

After the death of her 90-year-old mother in July 1962, Minnie Caldwell left Jubilee Terrace and moved to the other side of the viaduct, renting 5 Coronation Street.

On the morning of 18 January 1968 the residents of Victoria Street and Coronation Street woke to the roar of the dreaded bulldozer. For Ena Sharples the impossible was happening: the Mission hall that had been her home for 30 long years was going to be pulled down. Several attempts had been made to save the building. At one stage a community centre had been opened in the hall to encourage people to use the place, but enthusiasm soon waned and the Council withdrew support for the project. The congregation now seldom rose above six and the Mission committee were told that the Mission on Victoria Street would have to house them. With the Mission and Elliston's factory being demolished the people of Coronation Street began to wonder when the massive steel ball would finally turn in their direction.

CHAPTER 9

1968-1976: THE CHANGING FACE OF WEATHERFIELD

VALERIE
Hair Stylist

PERMS

TINTING

DYEING

RAZOR CUTTING ETC.

9, Coronation Street,
Telephone: WES 5137.

Valerie Barlow opened her hair salon in 1962. She soon had the residents complaining as the street had to be dug up to lay cable for her new telephone — the first residential phone in Coronation Street.

JACKSON'S CHIP SHOP had started business in Eli Thurgood's front parlour at 156 Victoria Street in 1903. By the year 1968 it had been transformed into a thriving outlet, incorporating the old house at 156 as well. The shop made the best battered fish in Weatherfield, and it could be eaten on the premises if so desired. Unfortunately, the shop stood in the way of the Council's redevelopment scheme and, like the Mission of Glad Tidings which it backed onto, it was demolished.

Frank and Mary Jackson relocated their business to 17 Rosamund Street without too many changes to their clientele, but the demolition of the Mission heralded the end of an era for the non-conformist community. The Council took advantage of the dwindling congregations to flatten most of the Victorian chapels and missions in the area.

With her Mission demolished, caretaker Ena Sharples filled her days helping to run the OAP clubhouse on Nightingale Street. When the Council announced their plans to build a car park on the site, Ena led the pensioners in a sit-in outside the Town Hall. The police were called in to break up the demonstration and Ena was thrown into a police cell for the night.

≋ VALERIE BARLOW — AFRAID OF THE ≋ UNKNOWN

'Sometimes I do feel that I'd like to look out of the window, and see a tree instead of a wall. I'd like to collect washing off a line that wasn't soiled with dirt and soot, maybe have a garden instead of a window box. But how much sympathy and feeling can you get out of a house full of mod cons when you're feeling low and depressed and can't cope?'

Kenneth Barlow had always promised his wife Valerie that they would move out of Coronation Street. Ever since they had first married in 1962 he had talked of the semi-detached, three-bedroomed house, with a garden, that was waiting for them somewhere. At first Val had listened with eager anticipation, then, as the years went by, she came to realize that the longed-for dream home was just that — a dream.

It wasn't that they couldn't afford to move. They had bought Number 9 Coronation Street after their honeymoon so that they could be near Ken's father at Number 3 and her uncle at Number 1. Ken earned a good salary as a graduate teacher and up to the birth of the twins the hair salon she had run in the front parlour enabled them to save very well. Why then hadn't they moved?

Her Uncle Albert was still living in the street, but he could be persuaded to move with them; Valerie spent so much of her time cooking for him it might be easier all round if the old man lived with them anyway. No, he wasn't the real problem. Although Ken had been born in the street he had no sentimental feelings about the area, he had once told her that the houses should be treated like matches: only used once then thrown away. He always seemed quite keen to move although Valerie knew there was no danger of him taking the initiative and making the first move. She knew that was down to her. So why didn't she make that first step towards a move?

Fear was the answer. Fear of the unknown. This was her life, what she knew and understood; tight little communities, nosy oppressive neighbours who knew all your business. The hair-netted old battle-axe who would shout at you for hanging washing out on the Sabbath, the local pub with its narrow-minded customers and the corner shop with its easy credit system and the sympathetic

Valerie Barlow had spent her whole life choking on fumes in back streets. The idea of a house with a garden was very appealing, but could she turn her back on her responsibilities?

shopkeeper. She knew who to trust, who to avoid and who needed help when it was cold and the landlord had put the rent up. A semi just wouldn't hold the same love that a terraced house stood for. She would be alone — and vulnerable. Would she be able to run next door for a cup of sugar or a shilling for the meter? Would she be able to leave the twins with someone when there was only five minutes until the butcher shut and Ken's tea had burnt? Would there really be a butcher as good as Piggott's?

That was why she couldn't move. The fear of the unknown was far greater than of the known. Everyone knew Val Barlow in Coronation Street and that was the way she liked it.

The Council were proud of the maisonettes constructed on the old Elliston factory/Mission Hall site on Coronation Street. Seven houses were built, three of which were bungalows designed for pensioners and four were two-storey homes for families. Building was completed in 1968 and local families were given first consideration in their allocation. The Barlows decided to sell their home at

Number 9 Coronation Street and rent one of the new maisonettes: Number 14. Ena Sharples was allocated one of the flats, but soon moved out after the Council told her she could not hold religious meetings in her sitting room. A gap left between the maisonettes led to the new shopping arcade, which had been built on Victoria Street.

For the first few months the homes were envied by other residents, but then troubles began, the structures began to crack and the ground floor maisonettes started to become damp.

Not much was yet known of the aspiring singer, Rita Littlewood, who was struggling to make a living working at the local Orinoco Club.

⤛ RITA SINGS THE BLUES ⤜

'They named a sherry trifle after me at one Labour Club I played.'

Ginger Rogers danced on air, her elegant gowns filled the screen as her partner twirled her around smoothly. Ginger had poise, elegance and beauty. Rita Littlewood longed to be like her. At the age of four, dressed in a homemade Shirley Temple frock, her hair dressed in ringlets by Auntie May, Rita had looked down on the other children in the talent contest; none of them had red hair like her.

Amy Littlewood had no time for her stage-struck daughter's fiery temperament. She regarded her passion for the stage as a passing phase that had to be endured, but not encouraged. Her sister, May, on the other hand saw the talent in Rita that was just waiting to explode upon a stage. It was May who took Rita to the cinema and played the parlour piano as Rita struggled along with the song lyrics bought from the local music shop.

So what did qualifications matter? It was almost certain that Judy Garland had no qualifications. As Amy sat weeping in her chair for what might have been a glowing career for her daughter at secretarial college, Rita slipped her music sheets into an attaché case and auditioned for theatrical agent Harry Stone. Her voice had improved with age, her body had filled out and she had learnt how to wear a tight sweater to her advantage. She may not have won the contest as Shirley Temple but she had won a place on Stone's books.

The Orinoco Club was a sleazy place, the clientele were rough, to say the least, and the wages she earned barely covered her fare across Manchester from Fallowfield to Weatherfield. Rita's partner, Julie, tried to get her into her lodging house, but the landlady thought any girl who played the trombone must be trouble and refused to take her in. So each night Rita and her trombone made the long journey across town. She was actually considering dropping the trombone; it was hard work playing it as she tap-danced and she was finding more and more that she needed her hands free to slap down the more forward members of the audience. It was

The working man's heroine, Rita Littlewood, was the toast of nightclubs and sleazy bars all over Manchester.

amazing what the sight of fishnet stockings did to quite tame-looking men.

Being classed as an 'exotic dancer' tended to give men the wrong idea. Harry Bates had certainly got the wrong idea on their first date. Just because a woman shows bits of her body on stage, it doesn't mean she's going to be willing to do the same off-stage. She'd been surprised to see him again the next night; no one she had known before had returned for a second knee in the groin.

The relationship progressed and she moved in with Harry in 1968. He was rarely home as his work took him away a lot. That may have been one of his attractions. It meant Rita had the flat to herself on the evenings she wasn't singing, and as long as she got the kids off to school all right, she could return to bed for an extra lie-in in the mornings. They weren't her children. Although she now called herself 'Mrs Bates' there had never been a wedding service and her finger bore no ring. It had been the children who made up her mind to move in with Harry. She would have been happy seeing him whenever he wasn't building motorways, but the kids obviously needed a mother to look after them, and Rita had no objection to stepping into their dead mother's shoes. Gail was a quiet reserved child and Terry was a smasher — cheeky, loud, boisterous and a right bundle of trouble. All the things that Rita had been to her mother. Over the years she stopped thinking of Terry as someone else's child; she loved him as her own son and knew that he loved her. They would joke together, tell each other their problems and occasionally she would let him have some cheap wine and allow him to watch snatches of her act.

Shirley Bassey had now replaced Ginger Rogers as Rita's inspiration. The dresses were more low-cut and glittery, and had large slits up the thighs. Flamboyant earrings were popular, as were high heels and huskier, deep singing voices. Rita adapted to each change and at clubs all over Weatherfield she built up a following amongst the working men. The money she earned was average, the customers still treated her as if they had paid for her at the door, and the clubs still remained sleazy. But somehow, standing up on a stage with a microphone in her hand and a three-piece band behind her, Rita managed to keep her dignity. Ginger Rogers had taught her how to act like a lady; young Terry Bates was teaching her how to be a mother. One day she would find someone who would love and cherish her and treat her like a *proper* woman.

18-year-old Dickie Fleming ran off to Gretna Green to marry schoolgirl Audrey Bright. Setting up home at Number 3 Coronation Street in 1968, they had a happy life until Audrey's affair with Ray Langton led to divorce two years later.

Police Sgt Cyril Turpin took over at Tile Street police station in June 1969. He had served with the constabulary in Birmingham and had moved further North to please his wife Betty, who had been brought up in Tile Street as Elizabeth Preston. Her sister Maggie had recently bought the corner shop in Coronation Street while her alcoholic husband Les was away from home drying out in hospital. Betty wanted to help Maggie run the shop but Maggie objected to her bossy elder sister interfering, so Betty took a job as barmaid at the Rovers Return instead.

The Rovers pub changed considerably with the new decade. Landlord Jack Walker died at the age of seventy in June 1970, and his wife Annie decided to keep the pub on with the help of son Billy and Betty Turpin. For a long time the Walkers had been the only true parents that young, orphaned Lucille Hewitt had known.

⇖ THE BLOSSOMING OF LUCILLE HEWITT ⇗

'Me mam were taken when I were a kid, I were thrown into care and me dad got squashed to death by a van. What 'ave I got to be thankful for? All I've got is me. It's a pity I don't get on with meself very well.'

Little Lucille Hewitt was thoroughly spoilt by the people of Coronation Street. When her mother died shortly after her tenth birthday, the local women had helped care for the young girl until she was sent to a children's home by her father who felt he couldn't cope. It seemed to Lucille that everything she held dear had been taken from her. In return, at the home she was given a hard bed in a drafty dormitory with no one to hug, no one to kiss her goodnight, and no one to give her comfort when the nightmares came.

Lucille was only allowed to return home to Number 7 Coronation Street when her father Harry announced his engagement to Concepta Riley. Concepta was the resident barmaid at the Rovers Return, and Lucille found her soft Irish accent romantic. She was thrilled to be Concepta's bridesmaid and was delighted to inherit Concepta's parents as her own grandparents. As the Hewitts honeymooned, the Riley family showed Lucille the delights of the Irish countryside. Lucille felt that their garage cum village shop would be her ideal home.

However, it was a different story three years later when it came to the family moving to Ireland to live permanently and Lucille refused to leave Weatherfield. She used her schooling as an excuse, but really she dreaded the idea of being isolated in the country with Concepta and her baby stepbrother Christopher who had won the family's affections and made her feel alienated and overlooked.

From school uniform to midi then mini-skirt, Lucille Hewitt shocked many of the older residents by following the latest fashions. On her eighteenth birthday her adopted guardian Jack Walker bought her a psychedelic dress with a hole in it that showed off her stomach.

Jack and Annie Walker, licensees of the Rovers, took Lucille into their home, allowing her to make a bed-sit of Concepta's old room. As the years passed she came to look upon them as Auntie Annie and Uncle Jack and they treated her just like a daughter. One of Lucille's proudest moments occurred on the stage at the Viaduct Sporting Club when she won the local talent contest singing the song *My Guy*. The contest win hadn't made Lucille treasure the evening, it was the fact that Uncle Jack had told her how proud he had been of her and her lovely voice.

Lucille, like most girls of her age growing up in the Swinging Sixties, was heavily influenced by pop music. She often played truant from school to work in a music shop and regularly hitched lifts on lorries to London to see her latest pop heroes playing in concert. She was nearly expelled from school for having 'Brett Falcon Fan Club' tattooed on her wrist. Brett was a local lad who had become a pop star and he had told her she could run his fan club. She had the tattoo done to prove to her school friends her high status.

Irish Concepta Riley went against her parents' wishes to marry out of her faith. However, Harry Hewitt took instruction from the Catholic priest and their son Christopher, born in August 1962, was brought up a Catholic.

The late Sixties found Lucille becoming disenchanted with her elders' authority, and she soon began to rebel against Auntie Annie's plans for her future. Annie hoped she would meet a nice boy from a respectable background and become the perfect housewife, posh enough to own a set of fish knives. Lucille, however, found herself attracted to the sort of men who treated her badly and left her emotions in tatters. She made friends with hippie Robert Croft and helped his commune set up in residence at Number 11 Coronation Street while the main householder, Elsie Tanner, was away.

To Annie's horror, Lucille moved in with the band and spent days and nights meditating and talking about the meaning of life. Annie had read in the newspaper about the flower people and their loose morals, and fearing for Lucille's mind, and particularly her body, she complained to the land-lord and the hippies were moved on.

The next group Lucille attached herself to were gypsies who set up camp on the croft by the Red Rec. Her efforts to befriend them were frustrated by their wariness of her. As far as they were concerned she was a do-gooder who was trying to ease her conscience in offering them financial help. They refused her charity, but were grateful when she tried to help them when the local men attacked their camp in an attempt to get them to move on. Lucille was furious when the police sided with the troublemakers and moved the gypsies on to Bury. When a policeman told her to stay at home with 'her sort' she angrily threw a brick through the window of his panda car.

The only authority that Lucille accepted was suprisingly that from the

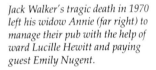

Jack Walker's tragic death in 1970 left his widow Annie (far right) to manage their pub with the help of ward Lucille Hewitt and paying guest Emily Nugent.

church. Ena Sharples attempted to guide her spiritually through life and in times of trouble Lucille always sought out Ena to talk things through with her. For a while, in the early Seventies, Lucille served as a helper at the Salvation Army. She surprised her friends by attending church services and openly declaring her faith in God. However, after a set back with an old man who refused to let her 'help' him Lucille left the Army. She did, however, remain true to her faith.

When romance blossomed, Lucille was adamant that she wanted to get married at St Mary's Church. Gordon Clegg from the corner shop had proposed marriage to her in 1969. She had readily accepted and even her Auntie Annie was pleased as Gordon had a good job as a qualified account-ant. Lucille was pleased that Gordon respected her wishes not to have sex before they were married. While outwardly giving the impression of being a modern girl living in the new permissive society, Lucille clung to the values Ena had instilled in her. Sadly, Gordon let her down and told her that he did not want to marry her as she was trying on her wedding dress, only a week before the ceremony. She was heartbroken. Gordon soon left the area to go to work in London and Lucille began to wonder if there was a true God anyway.

Lucille left Weatherfield in the summer of 1974. A visit to her step-mother, Concepta, and her new husband (Harry having died in 1967) turned from days into weeks and from weeks into months. The Ireland of Lucille's youth remained the same. The spring still flowed in the back garden, the villagers were still the same friendly people. Weatherfield was far away and Lucille decided that that was where it could stay. She was sick of breathing in dirty fumes, every morning she filled her lungs with the crisp air and decided that if she did ever return to her home town it would only be for a visit. Home was where the heart was and that certainly wasn't Weatherfield.

Trainee accountant Gordon Clegg fell for Lucille's independent streak.

＊

Local blonde Bet Lynch left her job in a launderette to join the staff of the Rovers as junior barmaid. On the other side of the viaduct in Jubilee Terrace, the Flying Horse public house was the only building left standing after all the old tenement terraces had been demolished. The viaduct had been blocked off after the rail disaster of 1967, and with the demolition of Jubilee Terrace, it was completely bricked up. It was decided to build new houses in the terrace and the architects moved away from the disastrous tower blocks of the late Sixties to design modern houses that maintained the old communities they were replacing. The new houses on Jubilee Terrace became a showpiece for the Council.

Bet Lynch and Hilda Ogden had a good time during an outing to Preston Guild in 1972.

Life in Weatherfield never stayed quiet for long and in January 1971 Valerie Barlow was tragically electrocuted by a faulty hairdryer and their mai-sonette caught fire. Their home was gutted and the insurance inspector investigating after-wards found major structural defects in the whole building, and recommended that they all be condemned. Val's husband Ken moved in with her uncle Albert Tatlock and decided that

The Barlow family moved into their maisonette in 1968. Three years later the children, motherless, were sent to Glasgow to be brought up by their grandparents.

his young children would be better cared for by their grandparents who lived in Scotland.

The residents of Coronation Street were in uproar later in 1971 when the Council announced plans to build a warehouse and community centre, on the site of the maisonettes. No one objected to the centre but the thought of an enormous warehouse being situated directly opposite their homes on Coronation Street filled them with horror and brought back reminders of Hardcastle's and Elliston's factories. Local campaigners organized sit-ins on the site and public demonstrations. They were won round by the assurances of the Public Relations man from the mail-order company that was going to build and open the warehouse. The PR man kept his promises made to the residents, and the work force was recruited from the houses around the building, while the bosses spent most of their time working in the London head office. Ken Barlow was offered the job of running the warehouse when he complained to chairman Sir Julius Berlin about the amount of noise created by lorries travelling to and from the loading bay.

≈ IVY TILSLEY'S PACT WITH GOD ≈

'I may be hard-faced and I might well have a sharp tongue but do you really believe I have a heart of stone?'

With its company logo of a Union Jack, emblazoned over the works' entrance, the Mark Brittain Mail Order Warehouse was opened by company director Sir Julius Berlin on 19 May 1971. One of the first of the new employees to walk through the door was Mrs Ivy Tilsley, née Nelson, of Inkerman Street. Ivy had been taken on at the warehouse along with her neighbour and drinking partner from the Red Lion, Edna Gee, as a checking assistant. Their job was to check thoroughly every garment before it was packed to be sent off to the customer. It made a change from working at the pickle factory.

Ivy had lived in Inkerman Street for 15 years and rarely missed her native Rochdale. She had never even heard of Weatherfield back in the Fifties. Then she had been quite carefree, enjoying the benefits of being an only child in a house of honest hard workers. She had been brought up in anticipation of finding a husband and having a big Catholic family. Her mother's biggest regret was that she could only have one child, but as soon as Ivy could crawl Alice Nelson instilled in her young mind the notion that the more children she had the happier she would be in her life.

The record *Rock Around the Clock* had revolutionized young Ivy's world back in 1955. Over night she had become a rocker, backcombing her dyed blonde hair, stuffing falsies down her cleavage and trading the night spots of her native Rochdale for the bright lights of Manchester. On the dance floor with her mates, Ivy forgot all about the clock factory where she worked and willed herself to become part of the music, to be so in tune with the beat that she lost her identity in it. Ivy lived for her Saturday nights, the Palais, Babycham and, most of all, Elvis.

Herbert Harrison Tilsley was a Teddy Boy, with his hair slicked back, his feet crammed into his heavy brogues and his comb ever ready. Hanging around the Palais with his mates he never had any trouble scoring with the hobble-skirted, bobby-socked girls. Herbert had been seeing Ivy for over six months and secretly hoped she would be 'the right girl' his mam was always talking about. He had a feeling that under all that hair she was a sensible lass and, unlike her empty-headed mates, that she was exactly what he was looking for — someone sensible to settle down with.

'She's a Lassie from Lancashire' was Ivy Tilsley's favourite tune. She would whistle it as she walked to work in Coronation Street every day, swinging her handbag as she went.

The year was 1955, the world was changing fast. Since they had first met at the Palais, Churchill had resigned, James Dean had died in a car crash, Princess Margaret had been forced to reject Captain Peter Townsend, and Bert and Ivy had watched their first 3–D movie together. Bert decided to waste no more time; he was going to have to make his move and propose. But would she accept?

Ivy had made a pact with God. She knew it was against the rules, she felt wrong to bargain with the Almighty, but Ivy was desperate. She knew that Bert loved her. He was kind, considerate, understanding and patient and the way he called her 'my sweet' warmed her heart. All the same she knew he longed for a child as much as she did. He would never blame her for the three miscarriages but somehow she still felt guilty. Ivy kept blaming herself. Each night she had asked God why she had suffered the loss of her precious babies. She had grown obsessed with babies, hearing the poor little mites next door crying themselves to sleep every night she had to be restrained from going round and giving the ungrateful Mrs Harrison a piece of her mind.

Ivy had promised God that she would stay away from the dance halls and pubs on Saturday nights so she could attend two Masses on Sunday mornings.

Because of her previous experiences, Ivy was admitted to hospital in the sixth month of her 1958 pregnancy. She and Bert had been married for two years, they had never used birth control as they both wanted a large family, but instead they had nothing but emptiness.

The baby's cries would have been music to Ivy's ears. But she couldn't hear them, the baby's position inside her had meant a Caesarean operation under general anaesthetic. When she came to, in the neat hospital bed, she was alone. Immediately she felt that the baby must be dead.

Bert was with her when the nurse brought the baby in, wrapped up in a tight white bundle. Ivy cried with joy when she took her son in her arms, she kissed him, touched him, smelt him and hugged him. The doctor had told her that she would never be able to have another child but she didn't care; she had her little Brian John and nothing else mattered any more.

Cars were now commonplace in Weatherfield, every other household owned one and those who didn't used the corporation buses that had replaced the trams, although some old tram lines could still be clearly seen in the streets. Gradually all the old terraced streets were being tarmacked over. Sir Julius campaigned for the tarmacking of Coronation Street but Councillor Len Fairclough, who lived at Number 9, used his influence on the Highways' Committee to stop the plan. He felt strongly, like many other residents, that the cobbles were an important part of Weatherfield's industrial heritage.

Neighbours Annie and Minnie viewed the new Mark Brittain warehouse with distrust. They had both worked in mills and the sight of an industrial building brought back unhappy memories.

Violence seemed to be on the increase in the early Seventies as gangs of unemployed youths, who had left Bessie Street School with little or no qualifications, became bored with looking for work. They yearned for some excitement and found it by vandalising, stealing and mugging. The senior citizens reminded everyone that an element of violence had always been part of Weatherfield life, but now it was more out in the open and it was covered by the local press and statistics were being kept. The residents of Coronation Street suffered like everyone else: barmaid Bet Lynch was found bleeding in a back alleyway after a mugger had left her for dead; pensioner Albert Tatlock was beaten up at the new community centre and even haughty Annie Walker was confronted in her bedroom by two thugs who demanded money from her.

Three local boys, who often played truant, terrorized the area for three weeks in October 1975. Their rampage of crime and destruction left houses ransacked, cars stolen, windows smashed, pensioners jostled and two women dead. The women, Edna Gee and Marilyn Fern, died in the fire that completely gutted the Mark Brittain Warehouse. It had been started by a cigarette left in the stock room by the lads who had spent the night there. The three appeared at juvenile court and were later sent to Borstal.

The period from 1968–1976 holds the record with the police for the highest number of murders committed in Weatherfield. Two of these murders directly affected everyone in Coronation Street. Elsie Tanner had returned from America after the break up of her six-month-old marriage. Her husband Steve followed a short time later, and pleaded with her to return to him. During his stay in Manchester, Steve was brutally murdered. The inquest arrived at a verdict of 'death caused by persons unknown' and the case was covered by all the national newspapers. Two years later, on Christmas Eve 1970, Steve's old army buddy Joe Donnelli admitted to the murder before shooting himself. Len Fairclough had been the police's main suspect in the Tanner investigation as his possessive love for Elsie was well known. Len also became the main suspect when a woman was found murdered in his house. The woman, Lynne Johnson, had turned to Len, as her local Councillor, for help in escaping her violent husband. Len spent a week being interrogated by the police before her husband confessed to the murder.

Upper Edward Street, the main road situated next to the park, was renamed Curzon Street in honour of Mayor Curzon who died while still in office in 1971. Two years after his death, Weatherfield ceased to be part of Lancashire and became absorbed into Greater Manchester. The Town Hall now referred to the Manchester authorities and, now that the town was relegated to a borough, the office of Mayor was abandoned. The last Mayor of Weatherfield to be appointed was Post Office supervisor Alf Roberts who chose as his Mayoress his old friend Annie Walker. During their term of office they met Princess Alexandra at the opening of the 1973 Manchester Festival.

A new registry office was opened on Curzon Street, between the Laughing Donkey public house and St Mary's church. Faithful chapel and church worshippers reflected that it was a sign of the times that more and more couples were marrying in the registry offices. Religious congregations were diminishing and the media's preoccupation with 'free love', drugs and sex encouraged young people to turn their backs on the Church and God. Lay preacher Ernest Bishop often found his congregation at the Victoria Street Mission consisted of only his wife Emily and the organist.

Edna Gee and husband Fred celebrated her fortieth birthday in October 1975. The next day Edna lost her life in a fire. Fred served at the Rovers as resident potman from 1976 to 1984.

Blanche Hunt sold up her corset business and moved to the Midlands in January 1976 to run a country club owned by her old boyfriend, Dave Smith.

◁ DEIRDRE TAKES THE PLUNGE ▷

'Look at me, what am I doing? Popping off round the corner to get married. And then it will be round the next corner lookin' for somewhere to live an' then round the next takin' the kids to school.'

Blanche Hunt could not understand where her daughter Deirdre had got her stubborn streak. It had always been there, hidden beneath the surface. She often recalled the tantrum Deirdre had thrown in the middle of town when Blanche had refused to let her have a puppy. The child had clung to a lamppost and had refused to move until Blanche, in conciliation, had bought a goldfish. And now, fourteen years later, Deirdre was being just as stubborn.

Deirdre Hunt left school at 16 with 'O' Levels in English, Maths and General Science. She went straight into Weatherfield Commercial College to study typing and secretarial skills.

However, Deirdre at 20 was a calmer personality than Deirdre at six. She sat perfectly still in her bra and pants, on the fold-away chair, telling her mother she would not be wearing the wedding gown that Blanche had slaved over for the past two months. It was Deirdre's wedding day and she was adamant that she would become Mrs Ray Langton in her fawn two-piece suit, even though it had gravy spilt on it.

It had all been different only two weeks previously, when she had been about to marry Billy Walker. After a courting period, an engagement, and even a warring period when down-to-earth Blanche had clashed with snotty Annie Walker, Deirdre had finally entered the jilting period. With 19 days to go before the lavish wedding at St Mary's, Deirdre had suffered the normal nerves and doubts of a bride-to-be. Would she make a good publican's wife, how would she cope with having domineering Annie as a mother-in-law? Was she too young for 36-year-old Billy? When she voiced these fears to Billy he had agreed to give her time to think, but when she continued to have doubts he had packed his bags and left for Jersey to run a wine bar.

It was then that Ray Langton had started to get to her. Everyone else cautiously treated her with kid gloves, but tactless, big mouth Ray Langton made jokes at her expense, taunted her about Billy and asked her what it was like to be on the shelf at twenty. Unfortunately, Deirdre couldn't easily escape Ray's remarks as he was a partner in the firm where she worked as a secretary. She tried to be professional and to keep calm about the situation, but when Ray refused to stop, something snapped inside her. All the tension of the last few weeks was suddenly released from her and she smashed her typewriter against a wall. She then flung open the filing cabinet and scattered all her neat filing into the air. Slapping an astonished Ray across the face, she resigned in style.

A week later she married Ray. Everyone who knew the couple were amazed at the turn about in their relationship. Try as she did, Deirdre found she could not completely explain her feelings to Blanche. She realised now that Ray was the reason she couldn't marry Billy; she had always loved him and his snide remarks after Billy's departure had been his way of telling her he loved *her*.

There were no doubts this time, no clouds on the horizon. Deirdre knew she could manage wayward Ray, she could see aspects of his personality that others couldn't. It was true he had been in Borstal, that he'd wrecked a marriage and that he had made many sexual conquests. He was basically a male chauvinist with a one-track mind, who spent all his time in the pub and watched every United home game. But on the plus side he had fire, romance, passion and energy. Deirdre knew she would never know where she stood with Ray, but it would be fun all the same.

Raymond Anthony Langton had drifted into a life of crime after the death of his mother Mary, before he went straight and was taken on to work for Len Fairclough.

Ernest and Emily were one of the few couples to be married at Mawdsley Street Chapel, where they exchanged vows on Easter Monday 1972. Their neighbours and friends who married at a similar time mainly did so at the registry office. Ken Barlow married his second wife, Janet Reid, in a civic service, as did Ray and Deirdre Langton. Elsie Tanner married mechanic Alan Howard in a registry office in 1970, and her son Dennis had married two years previously in the same building. Dennis left the area with his bride Jennifer to

Newcastle-born Alan Howard set up hairdressing salons in and around Manchester and finally settled down to marry Elsie Tanner in July 1970. Three years later their marriage was over.

Leslie and Margaret Clegg bought Number 15 in April 1968. They had lived in Birmingham since the war, though Maggie was a native of Weatherfield.

Ernest and Emily Bishop married at Mawdsley Street Chapel. From left to right: Len Fairclough (who gave Emily away), Bet Lynch (bridesmaid), groom and bride, Lucille Hewitt (bridesmaid) and Ken Barlow (best man).

live in Bristol and the Howards also left Weatherfield to go and live in Alan's native Newcastle, where Elsie had been offered a job as a warehouse supervisor.

Maggie Clegg, who had run the Coronation Street corner shop for six years, left England in 1974 to start a new life in Africa. Her sister Betty was left in charge of the shop, which she rented out to the Hopkins family who were Welsh. It was Granny Megan Hopkins who found Gordon Clegg's birth certificate hidden in one of Maggie's drawers. She gave it to Betty, letting her know in no uncertain terms that she knew Gordon was Betty's son. The Hopkins then used the information to reduce the rent of the shop and Betty was forced to tell Gordon that she was his real mother. To her delight, he readily accepted her and happily threw the Hopkins family out. Betty was relieved, though, that she had kept her secret from husband Cyril all their married life. He had died of a heart attack shortly before her sister Maggie emigrated.

When Ena's lifelong friend Minnie Caldwell moved out of Number 5 Coronation Street after making the decision to retire to Whaley Bridge, Ena Sharples looked back over the changes they had experienced together. The trains had stopped running and the old mills were now derelict or had been converted into modern factories. Gone were the days when the missions were packed every Sunday and decimalisation had replaced the old currency. Ena hoped that she wouldn't have to live through too many more changes; as she grew older she realized the value of clinging on to what was familiar. She prayed that the Weatherfield Council would realize that too.

Teenager Tricia Hopkins remained at the corner shop after her family left under the cover of night in 1975. She shared the flat above the shop with workmate Gail Potter.

CHAPTER 10

1976-1983: A TIME OF CHANGE

Coronations Street's entry in the Council's Jubilee Carnival of 1977 was struck by disaster when the lorry failed to start in time for the procession.

FOR JUST OVER a year, from October 1975 to November 1976, the shell of the burnt-down warehouse had remained vacant in Coronation Street. For the street's residents it was a constant reminder of the changing social climate; unemployment was rising, as were prices in the shops, supermarkets and pubs. Firms offering expensive hire-purchase repayments for goods were thriving and people were just getting back to a full working week.

As Ken Barlow walked to work each day, from his house at Number 1 Coronation Street across the way to the local community centre (which he ran) next to the warehouse, he was sadly reminded of his flat that had once stood on the site. It had been burnt down in 1971, after a fire from an electrical fault, which had killed his first wife Valerie.

Ken was one of the many local residents who were pleased to see the warehouse re-open, this time as a modern factory producing the latest denim fashions in jeans, skirts and jackets. Londoner Mike Baldwin, a sharp businessman, owned the factory and had arrived in 1976 bringing jobs to 36 locals by opening this, his second factory. The first operated in London's Bermondsey where he had grown up.

≥≤ MIKE BALDWIN COMES TO TOWN ≥≤

'Love me or loathe me, you've got to admit, I've got style.'

Michael Vernon Baldwin moved into Coronation Street in 1976 to supervise the building of his new factory and quickly established himself as a well-off entrepreneur with a ruthless streak.

These characteristics had helped Mike move from a back street in Bermondsey, South London, where he had a TV repair business in his bedroom, to being the owner of a substantial factory and a house in Coronation Street. In London, he already owned a denim factory not one hundred yards from his old family home.

In his absence, his factory was left in the capable hands of old school friend Paul Tapp. Mike's one fear was that his father, ex-docker Frankie Baldwin, would somehow wheedle his way into Paul's confidence and take advantage of Mike's absence to his benefit. Mike left Paul strict instructions that in no circumstances was Frankie to be regarded as part of the company — father or no father.

In Weatherfield, all went well for him. He had money to spend and a confident winning manner that soon lured Bet Lynch, the Rovers' barmaid, into his bed at Number 5, the house he had bought when Minnie Caldwell had left for Whalley Bridge. Here he spent his weekdays, returning at weekends to London where he lived with Anne Woodley, a divorcée, and her two sons.

With Bet in Weatherfield and Anne back in London, Mike had enough going on in his private life, but was not especially reluctant to enjoy the attentions of other local ladies who found him attractive.

Mike Baldwin — cocky, flashy and always out for number one.

Meanwhile Mike was out to make some changes and his positive style and attitude, and his free morality, did not please the older residents. When he employed Ray Langton and Len Fairclough to gut Number 5 and carry out his modernization plans, Albert Tatlock and Ena Sharples saw it as the first step of his influence on Coronation Street, but Mike carried on his merry way, totally unaffected by the old-timers' resentment.

With the work completed, Bet moved into Number 5 and between them she and Mike fitted out the house with the most up-to-date furniture. This left Mike with two homes and two businesses, but his domestic life was sorted out unexpectedly when Anne called at Number 5. There she discovered Bet and was shocked by her bleached blonde hair and cheap scent.

Bet Lynch was happy and flattered to be taken up by Mike Baldwin, Coronation Street's most eligible bachelor, but she knew things couldn't last.

A sharp word with Mike resulted in Bet being quickly despatched and she was soon no longer part of Mike's plans.

Meanwhile, he concentrated his efforts in Weatherfield on business and added a retail outlet, Sylvia's Separates, to his factory interests. He'd been tipped off that the shop was for sale by Elsie Howard and having looked and liked what he'd seen, he decided to take the place over. Elsie may well have had reason to be pleased with herself and looked forward to a cosy little niche as manageress of the shop but, typically, Mike did not see things in the same light and told her she would be totally unsuitable as she was too old. Mike saw young Gail Potter as much more the image he wanted to project and he didn't think twice about passing Elsie over.

Many more were to suffer at Mike's arrogant hands and even though he made it up to Elsie by taking her on as a supervisor at Baldwin's Casuals, all who worked with him or came into contact with him agreed that Mike Baldwin was on the up and woe betide anyone who stood in his way.

During the period 1976-1983, even though money was tight, the residents of Weatherfield had a surge of patriotism. For Queen Elizabeth II's Silver Jubilee in 1977 various events were held to mark the happy occasion. Most of the streets in the town had entered floats in the Council's organized parade. The subject matter chosen varied from street to street, while Raglan Street presented 'Our Roman Heritage', Weavers Row won the prize cup with their float, 'England in 2077', complete with a six-foot robot with eyes flashing red, white and blue.

The Coronation Street entry, 'Britain Through the Ages' had been tipped to win the contest with such notables appearing as Annie Walker as Elizabeth I, Ena Sharples as Queen Victoria, Ken Barlow as Sir Edmund Hillary and Albert Tatlock as his loyal sherpa, Tensing. Disaster struck when accident prone Stan Ogden, the float's driver, left the lorry's lights on all night and the battery went flat so the lorry wouldn't start.

The last of the terraced houses to be demolished under the 1968 redevelopment plan fell in the late Seventies. The homes nestling between Curzon Street and Rosamund Street made way for a huge shopping precinct in 1977. It was named the Queen's Shopping Centre in honour of the Jubilee and boasted large offices, shop premises, a library, a new DHSS office and a much needed health clinic.

The Community Centre on Coronation Street played host to a Jubilee Glamorous Grannie contest and a bouncing baby show. Six-month-old Tracy Langton, won the baby contest, had been one of the town's first Jubilee babies, having been born on 24 January 1977. Her mother Deirdre soon found herself left alone with little

Ray and Deirdre Langton were delighted with the birth of their jubilee baby Tracy in January 1977.

Tracy when her husband took a plumbing job in Holland after the break up of their marriage in November 1978.

Deirdre, now homeless, joined the long waiting list for a council house and was eventually allocated a one-bedroom flat on the 14th floor of Disraeli House, a run-down tower block. Luckily for Deirdre she was able to refuse it as she was taken in by neighbour Emily Bishop. Emily had been left a widow in early 1978 when her husband Ernest had been shot dead in a wages snatch at the factory where he worked.

Len Fairclough, the local councillor, lost his seat on the Council in glaring publicity in 1978. He had represented the St Mary Ward as an independent for 12 years. After the drunken revelry of fellow Councillor Alf Robert's stag night, Len was stopped by a policewoman for smashing a bottle of whisky in the street. When the policewoman cautioned him, he became abusive and made sexual overtures towards her. He was later cleared of being drunk and disorderly in court, but was forced to resign from the Council in disgrace. Len, recently married to nightclub singer, Rita Littlewood, then channelled all his energies into running his building business.

At the time of Len Fairclough's arrest, Alf Roberts' friendship with local shopkeeper, Renée Bradshaw had blossomed into marriage. She owned the corner shop on Coronation Street, and after their marriage, Alf neglected his work at the Post Office to help out behind the counter.

Len Fairclough and Rita Littlewood were married in April 1977. They honeymooned in Tenerife where singer Rita had a cabaret booking.

☙ ALF AND RENÉE ROBERTS' ❧ BRIEF HAPPINESS

'I've never been to an all-night party. The permissive society passed me by. I don't suppose I would have enjoyed it. I'll never know now will I?'

Renée Bradshaw turned to her native Weatherfield in 1976 to buy a flat for her younger brother Terry who was a plumber working for Len Fairclough in his building firm. The fact that she acquired the corner shop into the bargain was of little importance to her, but she soon found herself in a legal battle with Annie Walker when she applied to spice-up the image of the shop by opening an off-licence.

Annie saw the threat to the Rovers of another outlet for alcohol in the street, and vigorously opposed the licence. Renée won the day and the licence was granted by the Council, no doubt helped by Councillor Alf Roberts, who was a well-received visitor to the shop.

Alf and Renée became friends and when widower Alf, stolid and set in his ways, proposed to

Alf Roberts began to spend more and more time at Renée Bradshaw's shop and it wasn't long before love blossomed. Their happy marriage was cruelly ended when Renée was killed in a motoring accident in July 1980.

Renée Bradshaw had spent most of her life working in Lancaster as a supermarket check-out girl.

Renée while drunk at the Gatsby nightclub, she happily accepted. Next day, as the alcohol's effect left Alf with a hangover and feeling remorseful, he realized the importance of his drunken words and had to face up to the possibility of a marriage to someone he liked but did not love.

Steeling himself to right the wrong, Alf confessed to Renée that he had made a big mistake and wished to withdraw the proposal. Renée was disappointed, but worldly enough to agree that to proceed in the circumstances would be stupid.

They remained good friends, and a few months later, when Alf was spending more and more time at Renée's table, he proposed again and this time he meant it sincerely. They married on 20 March 1978, at the local Registry Office, but the reception was marred by an unseemly scuffle between Alf and Renée's stepfather Joe Hibbert, who loudly told Alf, in front of all the guests, that he must have been desperate to marry Renée, but then added as an afterthought that maybe Alf wasn't so silly as Renée was a woman of means. This was too much for the placid Alf and, to general encouragement, he waded in to lay Joe out on the floor.

Soon after their wedding Renée's love was put to the test when Alf underwent a personality change after a head injury he sustained when a lorry crashed into the Rovers and left him in a coma for two weeks. He recovered from his injuries, but was ill-tempered and irrational, often turning on Renée for no apparent reason. Eventually, he recovered fully after a course of psychiatric treatment.

To complete his recuperation the couple took a relaxing holiday at Grange, which they enjoyed so much they decided to sell up in Coronation Street and take on a sub post office in a rural area. Everything went well; they found a buyer for the shop and, with Alf's connections, found no trouble in securing a rural post office.

The future beckoned enticingly as they set off for a country pub to celebrate their good fortune. Thinking about the good times ahead, Alf drank just a little too much. Renée, who was learning to drive, suggested she should take the wheel and they commenced their journey home at a leisurely pace. Little did they realize that this would be their last trip together. Not long after setting off, they came to a roadworks with single-file traffic, and Renée, driving impeccably, waited for the green light. Halfway between the lights she stalled the car in the middle of the single lane and couldn't get it to re-start.

Alf decided to take over, and had just got out to take the driving seat when a massive lorry, now riding on the green light in his favour, thundered into the stationary car. Renée was hurled backwards, then forwards to finally end up slewed across both seats, bleeding and badly injured. Alf stood shattered in the road as the fire brigade, ambulance and the police arrived. As he stood holding the breathalyser in his hand, the news was broken to him that Renée was dead.

Local cabbie, Don Brennan, was widowed in 1978 when his wife Pat died of cancer. He was left to bring up three children alone.

Britain's first lady Prime Minister, Margaret Thatcher, came to power in 1979. Everyone in Weatherfield was keen to see what difference she would make to their way of life. With unemployment hovering just below three million, factories and small businesses continued to close down in the town. Even Mike Baldwin felt the pinch and was forced to close his London factory to keep the Weatherfield one going.

The Tilsley family moved to Coronation Street in 1979, buying Number 5 for £7,000. The house had been completely converted with the front and back parlours knocked into one and a brick fireplace installed as the room's focal point. Brian Tilsley married Gail Potter and they set up home with his parents after their marriage in November of the same year.

GAIL POTTER LEAVES HOME

*'All my life people have said I was just like me mam. Well I'm not.
I'm not that hard-faced, irresponsible or cheap.'*

Gail Potter came to live in Coronation Street in 1975, having just moved from home in a fit of anger, after her mother, Audrey, told her that Frank Peterson, whom she had always regarded as her father, wasn't her real dad.

As if that piece of news wasn't heart-rending enough, she also learned that legally she didn't even have a father in the true sense. Audrey was, at that time, free with her favours and Gail's father had been just one of a string of casual loves who had passed through her life. Audrey Potter was not exactly an immoral person, but she enjoyed a good time.

Stephen Potter, Gail's brother, had been born in 1956 when Audrey, at 16, was working as a waitress in a Manchester club. Half an hour's romp in the back of an old convertible had left her pregnant. If she knew the father's name she certainly wasn't going to tell her violent father Bobby. Audrey dreamed of babies and prams, but her father took no notice of her enthusiasm and arranged for a young couple from the street to take the baby off his hands. Audrey's protests were ignored, and faced with the prospect of being cast out, she finally had to agree to his plans.

Malcolm and Joyce Reid were thrilled to take on baby Stephen when he was born as they were unable to have children of their own. Audrey had

Audrey Potter had a colourful lovelife in her youth, which left her daughter Gail confused about her parentage and with a brother she didn't know existed.

Gail Potter, chirpy, trendy and just the person Mike Baldwin needed to run his clothes shop 'The Western Front' in Victoria Precinct.

Brian and Gail married in November 1979 in spite of Ivy Tilsley's objections on the grounds that Gail was not a Catholic.

to content herself with watching Joyce pushing Stephen around in his big pram and occasionally going to baby-sit.

It was only a year after Stephen's birth that Gail was conceived. This time Audrey fought tooth and nail for her child. Bobby was suffering from a terminal illness and knew he would soon leave Audrey's mother a widow. He agreed to let Audrey keep her child on the condition she stayed at home to look after her mother.

When Gail was two, in 1960, Audrey had dressed her in her best clothes to stand on the quayside to wave the Reids off as they set off for a new life in Canada. The heartache Audrey felt at the loss of her first child was softened by the warm, chubby little hand holding hers so tightly.

The only thing Gail really knew about her life was that Audrey was her mother and Nancy Potter, who lived next door at number 18 Bath Street, was her grandmother — on her mother's side of course.

Arriving in Coronation Street to work at the Mark Brittain Warehouse, she became friendly with Tricia Hopkins who occupied the flat over the corner shop. Tricia's parents had once owned the shop but had now moved on to be replaced by Gordon Clegg, who saw his two young tenants as the ideal people to staff the shop in his absence.

His assessment of their characters proved to be his undoing as the two dizzy girls, with nothing more on their minds than *Top of the Pops*, The Bay City Rollers and the latest 'look' to wear to the disco, allowed the shop to deteriorate into chaotic disorganization, with bills running up, stock not replenished and many dissatisfied customers. Gordon was obliged to end the arrangement abruptly and Tricia moved out. Elsie Howard, perhaps seeing in young Gail a similarity to herself at that age, helped her get work at Sylvia's Separates and took her into her home at Number 11 as a lodger.

What Audrey Potter, now living in Bury alone and working as a barmaid, may have thought of her young daughter in the clutches of the street's notorious man-eater was not known. Certainly, she would have seen no wrong in the aimless life of serendipity into which Gail had drifted. She was young, attractive and quite able to look after herself.

Probably Audrey did not even know her only daughter's circumstances but, as she observed her growing into womanhood, she may have taken great pleasure from Gail's apparent mirror-image of herself.

After the excitement of the Jubilee, the Weatherfield folk had a few years to wait for their next Royal celebration. In July 1981 street parties were held all over the town to celebrate the Prince of Wales' marriage to Lady Diana Spencer. The pupils at Bessie Street School, along with those at the newly opened comprehensive school on Regents Road, were all given their own special commemorative mugs. The residents of Coronation Street did not organize a street party as two days previously, on 27 July they had celebrated a wedding of their own — Ken Barlow, the street's romancer, had married Deirdre Langton. The couple set up home at Number 1 with Albert Tatlock, the uncle of Ken's first wife, Valerie.

The Ogdens' lodger, Eddie Yeats, had always seemed too preoccupied with drink and his manic money-making schemes with Stan Ogden to worry about women, but he became romantically linked with a fellow CB fan, Marion Willis, in February 1982. By the end of the following year, their up-and-down romance had finally turned into marriage.

Suzie Birchall and Gail Potter shared a room at Number 11, Elsie Tanner's house, in 1977 for about 18 months before Suzie went to London and got married.

Ken Barlow married Deirdre Langton on 27 July 1987, two days before the royal wedding of Prince Charles and Lady Diana Spencer.

～ EDDIE YEATS GOES STRAIGHT ～

'Me mam died while me dad were inside. I were left with me sister and her feller, who had form. I didn't stand a chance.'

Eddie Yeats came to Coronation Street on the recommendation of Jed Stone, an incurable, but good-hearted, petty criminal who had lodged with Minnie Caldwell. Inevitably, Jed's recommendation meant that Eddie associated with the criminal classes which, considering he was just out of Walton Gaol on remand, the lovable rogue could not deny.

He had called on Minnie Caldwell at Christmas 1974 to tell her that Jed Stone, her former lodger, had been required to spend Christmas with Her Majesty and was unable to turn the invitation down. Eddie stayed, cooked the Christmas dinner and, apart from the odd return to confinement at Her Majesty's pleasure, established himself as a firm resident of the street and the Rovers.

It was when he arrived much later at Number 13, to lodge with Stan and Hilda Ogden, that he came to a haven where his criminal past was forgotten and he could forge a new life within, even if only just within, the law.

In Hilda he found the caring mother he had never had, and in Stan, who was as boozy, lazy and devious as Eddie himself, he found an ideal business partner in their window cleaning business — and drinking partner, in the Rovers, the Laughing Donkey and the Flying Horse. Eddie became almost like an older son to Hilda, whose own children had long left Coronation Street.

Romance seemed far away from Eddie's mind as he divided his time between making a living as a dustman and part-time window cleaner and being a hard drinking slob in his time off. Admittedly, he was always ready to chat about the girls with Fred Gee, the Rovers' cellarman, but in the main, Eddie's dreams stayed in the pub.

It was when he obtained a CB radio in early 1982 and entered the world of 'handles' and all the other mysterious jargon of the airwaves, that he first came across a girl whose radio handle was 'Stardust Lil'. His own handle, 'Slim Jim', was not reflected by Eddie's ample girth and his genuine life-style was not reflected by Slim Jim's aerial claims.

As exchanges between Slim Jim and Stardust Lil increased and took on a more personal nature, a date was arranged at which Eddie, freshly pampered and spruced, presented himself for the first time to Marion Willis, alias Stardust Lil. Like everything Eddie touched, the meeting was not straightforward. Eddie had obtained the keys of Mike Baldwin's luxury flat where Hilda was the cleaner, and, in Mike's absence passed himself off to Marion as a property owner and a man of means and good taste.

It was not long before Eddie had to come clean with the deception and Marion, luckily, forgave him. He soon proposed and put away for ever his scams and dodges as she moved in to lodge with Elsie Tanner at Number 11, next door.

Eddie Yeats got on well with everybody in the street, and always made time to speak to old-timers like Albert Tatlock.

Eddie Yeats was known to be an ex-convict, but he soon won his way into the Ogdens' hearts and became their surrogate son.

Those days of courtship were happy times for Eddie and Marion as they and the Ogdens enjoyed many evenings together and, apart from Marion getting pregnant, the only hitch in their otherwise blissful courtship came when Eddie, with the best intentions in the world, allowed one of Elsie Tanner's fancy-men to cheat them of their hard earned nest-egg, saved for their mortgage. Eddie, for once, was the victim and was led to believe the profit from the deal would more than double their money.

Eventually, Slim Jim and Stardust Lil tuned in to a common wavelength when they married in October 1983 and moved to Bury a couple of months later in December.

Patriotism reached fever pitch in the country as the British task force set off for the Falklands in April 1982. Amongst those on the high seas was Terry Duckworth, then a regular soldier with the paratroopers. Jack and Vera Duckworth welcomed the British victory and looked forward to his safe return home.

Inkerman Street, situated down by the canal, took on a new look in the early Eighties. The few occupants who still rented their homes cursed themselves for not accepting their landlord's offer in 1978 of buying their homes at rock-bottom prices. In 1983 they were given £1,000 to find other accommodation as part of the street was demolished to make way for an adult education centre. Those families who had bought their homes celebrated the generous Council compensation they received. The Duckworths used the £1,000 as a deposit for a mortgage on Number 9 Coronation Street, which they bought for £10,000. Their son Terry had left the army after the Falklands War and Jack and Vera looked forward to a fresh start in their troubled marriage.

⤴ VERONICA MEETS HER JAKE ⤵

'You're useless you are Jack Duckworth. Flamin' useless. Useless, idle and no good. If only I'd listened to my mother.'

The Duckworth family – Jack, Vera and son Terry — moved into Number 9 Coronation Street under a cloud of laughter and humilation in September 1983. As they moved their broken furniture into the house, the local residents commented that the area would definitely suffer from having the workshy, rowing Duckworths on their doorstep. Vera was highly ashamed of her chipped sideboard and three-legged table and wondered how she'd ever got herself into this position, married to idle Jack, working in a sweat-shop for the minimum of wages, and having a son who cared more about weight training than giving her a little extra in her housekeeping.

As a child, Jack Duckworth earned his keep by acting as look-out for his father, an unlicensed bookie. This early interest in betting remained with him and he became a regular but unlucky visitor to the turf accountant.

As a young teenager, Vera had expected so much more from life. Although she had left school with no formal qualifications and was forced to work in a candle factory, she had pinned her hopes on a rosy future for herself as she had blonde hair, good looks, long legs and a slim figure. Heads always turned when she tottered down the street in her high heels and she'd expected to catch the attentions of a wealthy businessman any day, but sadly it was not to be...

Vera Burton was stopped in her tracks as she and her pals from Moss Side in Manchester passed the Waltzer at Bingley's fun fair. It was 1957 and when the fair came to town Veronica, or Vera as she was known to her family and close friends, always looked forward to a week of fun and frolic in a setting ideal for her major enjoyment in life — the pursuit, conquest and exploitation of the opposite sex.

Vera dressed up for the occasion with high heels, skin-tight leopard-patterned tights and a broad wasp-waist belt. Topped with her peek-a-boo hairstyle, which echoed her role model, movie star Veronica Lake (Vera was actually christened Veronica after the Hollywood beauty), she was fully prepared to tackle any likely man that came her way.

It was in such a frame of mind that she looked up at the Waltzer and saw an immediate prospect. As the cars spun and twisted at frightening speed, there, jumping from car to car with reckless abandon, was an Elvis Presley lookalike who immediately fulfilled all Vera's aspirations. With banter for everyone, especially the attractive girls, he cut a fine figure with black trousers, cowboy boots and a sleeveless vest complemented by a sleek well-greased DA hair style, that was still immaculate in spite of his athletic jumps and cavorting on the Waltzer.

As the music died and the machinery slowly pulled to a halt, Vera grabbed her friend, Enid Crump, and jumped into the seat nearest her quarry who stood, with his feet straddling two cars, as he counted out the money from the last ride.

She noticed he had an American eagle tattooed on his forearm and was also quick to notice that the brass studs on his belt, which had a skull motif buckle, spelt out 'Jake' — a perfect name to match his style.

Vera and Enid nudged past deliberately to catch his eye and Vera was delighted to see that she'd been noticed when he casually offered her a piece of his chewing gum. Jake put on a special show in the next ride and not

Vera Burton married Jack Duckworth in 1957 thinking she was pregnant. But it was a false alarm and their son Terry wasn't born until 1964.

only collected her money at full speed but skilfully spun the half-crown into the air to catch it on the back of his hand and tell her that she'd won, and therefore the drinks were on him when the fair closed that night.

Never one to turn down an invitation, Vera stayed on as the lights around the fair went out one by one and Jake busied himself by putting up all the shutters and tarpaulins. Her expectations were high and when Jake stepped down from the Waltzer, a leather-studded jacket draped over his shoulders, and hailed her in a slightly American accent, she felt butterflies in her stomach.

The rest of the night

was an anti-climax. The 'drink' turned out to be a cup of coffee in a paper cup and a doughnut served from a mobile canteen at one end of the fairground and Jake, as displayed on his belt, proved to be either a spelling error or a deliberate attempt to deceive. All his companions referred to him as Jack.

The American accent shifted from Texas to Boston then eventually back to pure Rochdale as Jack told Vera what good fortune she'd had to meet up with him and how they were going to have a 'gas' together.

Telling Vera that his T-bird was out of action, so they'd have to walk, Jack took Vera back to her home above her father's greengrocer's — a distance of about half a mile that took about two hours as they stopped off in every convenient doorway for a kiss and a cuddle. No slow mover was Jack Duckworth, nor, for that matter, was Vera. Arriving at the shop front of Joe Lewis Greengrocer's, Jack took stock of the well-provisioned window display and decided that Vera's father may be worth a bob or two, and arranged to see Vera at the fair on the following night.

Vera couldn't wait for the next day to pass. At Butterworth's candle factory, where she worked, Enid confirmed that Vera had got a real 'catch' and Vera slightly embroidered the facts of last evening by saying they'd gone for a drive in Jack's T-bird and then wined and dined at a late-night club.

That evening, Vera returned to the fair, saw Jack performing his acrobatics on the Waltzer and opted to pass the time by a trip on the Big Dipper where she and Enid, who'd come in hope of finding someone for herself, screamed their way through several hair-raising rides. Then at the very top of the ascent, the cars stopped suddenly, leaving Vera and Enid up in the clouds with the wind whistling in their ears. Below, the panicking attendant tried to get things moving, but nothing happened. Jack, on the next site, looked up, waved to Vera, and disappeared into the engine room.

Next thing they knew, there was Jack, sure-footed as a cat, treading the narrow rail towards them as though he were walking on the beach at Blackpool. Telling them they had nothing to worry about, he miraculously produced two bottles of Pepsi from inside his leather jacket, handed round the cigarettes, and entertained them with thrilling stories of his life in the Army before joining the fun fair. Eventually power was restored and Jack helped them out of their carriage with the swagger of a hero.

Vera fell for Jack's style there and then, even when she noticed that the American eagle tattoo had now changed to an Indian Chief's head. She knew that Jack, with his phoney accent, delusions of grandeur and transfer tattoo, was the man for her. After a good-night coffee and a hot-dog at the refreshment caravan, Jack walked her home once again, but this time with no stops. They headed straight for Joe Lewis' potting shed where, for the first time Vera, and probably Jack, in spite of his publicity to the reverse, made love, amongst the tomatoes, begonias and Michaelmas daisies.

Their evening of passion was brought to an abrupt end when the faces of Joe Lewis and Amy Burton, Vera's mother, were observed by Jack through the dusty window of the shed.

Jack was shown the garden gate by the affronted greengrocer, and told never to show his face again. Vera was attacked by her mother, called a slut, and threatened with expulsion from the family home should such an event ever happen again.

Vera, terrified by Amy's threat and lambasted by Joe Lewis for the destruction of some of his best seedlings, did not go back to the fun fair and after a week it moved on. Jack looked back on a lucky escape, but felt a little jewel had been wrested from his hands — that is, until the letter from Vera tracked him down telling him of his impending fatherhood.

Jack did the honourable thing and he and Vera married on 19 August 1957. Whether he would have abandoned his promising career in show business and gone through with the marriage had he known Vera's pregnancy was a false alarm, will never be known. However, when their son Terry was born in 1964, and the marriage had lost its sparkle, Jack often blamed Vera for robbing him of his more exciting showbiz heritage.

Coronation Street waved goodbye to Ena Sharples, caretaker at the community centre, in 1980. She had always been a well-known figure in Weatherfield, and was feared at the Town Hall where she had a reputation as a sharp-tongued tyrant in her austere Victorian-style clothes, but was much loved by her neighbours, who towards her last years, saw her as a vulnerable, frail old lady. Ena left the area, at the grand old age of 81, to keep house for an old friend in Lytham St Anne's.

Towards the end of 1983, fortunes seemed to be on the upturn. The Conservative Party, led by Mrs Thatcher, won a second term of office and the profitability of businesses began to increase. Property values climbed and the price of a Weatherfield terraced house rose from £4,500 in 1976 to £13,000. Thatcherism was at its height, small businesses were being promoted, people were encouraged to buy shares, and everyone's aim was to work hard and reap the subsequent rewards.

Phyllis Pearce lost her house in Omdurman Street when it was demolished in 1982. She moved into a warden-controlled bungalow in Gorton Close, alone, having lost her fellow naturalist husband, Harold, in 1978.

CHAPTER 11

1983-1989: A TIME OF SORROW

Percy Sugden found his appointment as caretaker of the community centre in 1983 an ideal position to exercise his authority.

TO PERCY SUGDEN, the most important event for the residents of Coronation Street in 1983 was his arrival to take over as caretaker of the community centre. Now a widower, he had been offered early retirement from his job at Holmes Bakery where he'd been employed since leaving the army in 1945. Percy was now ready for a new role and preferably one with responsibility and an opportunity to exercise his authority.

The community centre had been one of the first built in Weatherfield when it was opened in 1971. But by 1983, when Percy took over, it had become rundown and outdated — its only sports facility was a decrepit ping-pong table. Its once busy recreation hall was now only used as a polling station at election time or for the occasional ballroom dancing session.

Percy saw an immediate opportunity to instill a little authority into the area when a spate of burglaries occurred. The closest to home was when Emily Bishop, from Number 3 Coronation Street, was burgled and the corner shop was raided. The overworked police force were encouraging security-minded people to start up homewatch schemes as a deterrent to the rising crime rate, and Percy was happy to establish a scheme in Coronation Street.

To a neighbourhood reared on honesty and unlocked back doors, Percy's innovation came as a shock, but modern lawlessness had made it necesssary.

But the early eighties were a grim time when death stalked Coronation Street and came to claim some of its longest-standing residents. Len Fairclough, now a man of property, with a brand new house he'd built at Number 7 Coronation Street, a thriving newsagents at the Kabin, and his own building business, met his end in a motorway smash. His widow Rita was left with a lot of questions unanswered and she discovered a secret affair.

Albert Tatlock, the street's oldest resident, whose memories went back over eighty years, died suddenly while on holiday with his daughter Beattie. His grumpy complaining was missed by all who knew and loved him for it. Ken and Deirdre Barlow became the new owners of Number 1 which had been in Albert's hands since 1919.

Albert's departure signalled the end of the Edwardian ambiance that prevailed in his long-standing home and Ken and Deirdre soon installed a luxury fitted-kitchen in place of the primitive scullery that had remained unaltered since 1902. Another relic of the past, Albert's wedding gift from his old friend Dinky Low, his splendid mahogany sideboard, was replaced with modern built-in shelving.

When Stan Ogden, from Number 13, died in November after a long battle against a debilitating illness, few of the clients on his window-cleaning round would have been aware of his passing. Stan had never been highly active in the business his wife Hilda had purchased for him, and, with the possible exception of visits to Clara Regan at Number 19 Inkerman Street, with whom Stan had a special relationship, he had not ventured out as often as he should with bucket and ladder.

In spite of his laziness, drunkenness and petty dishonesty, Hilda was devastated by his passing — through it all they had been good friends. She collapsed under the strain but was sustained in her hour of need by her neighbours, who all had a special place in their hearts for her and 'big Oggy'.

Alf Roberts, now a widower twice over, proposed to widow Rita Fairclough, but she felt she did not love him. But he made it to the altar for the third time in 1985 when he chose Audrey Potter to be his new wife. She had been helping him out in the shop and generally cheering him up in all respects, except for her rather cavalier attitude to her duties.

Albert Tatlock died in 1984, aged 88. Apart from the war years, he had spent all his life in Weatherfield.

Alf Roberts made the big step of converting the corner shop to a self-service supermarket in 1985, but even this did not enable him to compete with Bettabuy on a price basis.

The end of an era was clearly signalled when, in 1985, the old corner shop, which had remained virtually unchanged since the first incumbent, Cedric Thwaite, had dispensed milk from the churn in 1902, was completely restyled as a self-service supermarket to keep up with the times. People initially missed the personal service but soon got used to the new system. No sooner had Alf made the change than Rajiv Patel opened up his larger mini-market, which was open 24 hours, round in Rosamund Street. Sally Webster was taken on as one of Alf's first cashiers.

KEVIN WEBSTER SETTLES IN

'You an' me Sal, we're real. Not the past, not my family, or yours. Just you an' me.'

Kevin Webster came to Coronation Street in 1984 with his widower father Bill and sister Debbie. Bill was a builder who took over Len Fairclough's yard with an eye to property development. Seeing a future in the thriving area, Bill bought Number 11 from Elsie Tanner for £10,000 and in June 1984 they moved in.

Debbie was still at school and Kevin had left Bessie Street School without even a CSE. He was assigned a place on a youth opportunity scheme at Whitehead's Garage, but he was later made redundant as they'd found a cheaper apprentice and he got a job with Brian Tilsley at his garage. Despite his bickering with Debbie, Kevin was really happy in his new surroundings in Coronation Street.

Kevin Webster was left alone at Number 11 Coronation Street when his father moved to Southampton in 1985. He later lodged with Hilda Ogden.

When Bill courted Percy Sugden's niece, Elaine Prior, and marriage seemed likely, Kevin was not keen on the idea. He still had very fond memories of his mother, Alison, who had died of cancer in 1980, and felt Bill was being just a little inconsiderate to her memory. He was even more upset when Bill announced that they would be moving to Southampton after the wedding. The way Kevin saw it, Bill was riding rough-shod over the entire family to satisfy Elaine, and he decided he was staying put.

Although it would have been better for him to join in with the new Webster family and try to resume the old happy way of life, Kevin had a point to make and settled for an independent, self-supporting role as the angry young man of Coronation Street.

Bill, his new wife and Debbie moved out, leaving Kevin on his own in Number 11, which was eventually sold to the Claytons. Kevin went from lodgings with Emily Bishop, where he and fellow lodger Curly Watts did not cope too happily with their cramped accommodation, to an eventual haven with Hilda Ogden at Number 13. She provided him with all the comforts of home and doted on him like a long-lost son.

Mother hen Hilda was delighted when Kevin took up with pretty Michelle Robinson from the other side of the tracks and urged him to make something of the relationship and invite Michelle to tea. Kevin was really smitten by Michelle, but she just considered him as one of her many boyfriends.

Angrily he ditched her, much to Hilda's horror, and then he shocked his landlady and surrogate mum even further by taking up with Sally Seddon from Arkwright Street, whose family was well known to Hilda.

Sally was a pretty young thing, but she was following fast in the steps of her unsavoury family. Her father was a lorry driver, more often out of work than in, and her mother was a slattern struggling to make ends meet from the little money that her husband gave her, and whatever else she could take from Sally and her sister Gina.

Meeting Kevin was the best thing that had happened to Sally and, although she was still prepared to meet Terry Duckworth secretly behind Kevin's back, she really did love Kevin in spite of what she saw as his very straight-laced approach to life.

Kevin was now torn between his love for Sally and his respect for and gratitude to Hilda, who had given him all that his own family had been unable to. He watched on in anguish as Hilda and Sally traded insults. But Kevin had his mind set on Sally and was often obliged to make Hilda aware that if it came to a choice, Sally would win. Eventually Hilda mellowed sufficiently to allow Sally to move in as her second lodger.

There was a fraught settling-down period for the couple, when Hilda always suspected the worst and monitored their every move — especially

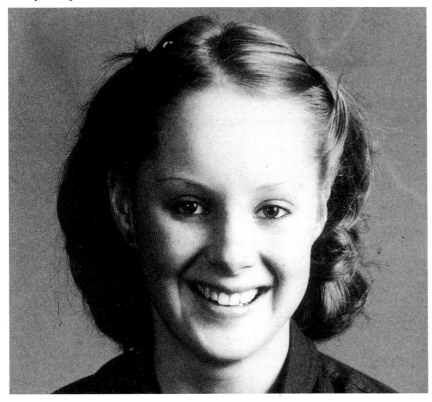

Sally Seddon was from the wrong side of the tracks. She joined Kevin to lodge with Hilda Ogden, who disapproved of Sally but was soon won round by the young lovers.

after lights out. But she eventually saw Sally for the pleasant, friendly young girl she was, in spite of her unfortunate family connections. Now, Hilda had a daughter and a son to care for, and right up until their marriage, she treated them as her family — honorary Ogdens.

After a brief spell living with Hilda after their marriage, Kevin and Sally moved to the flat over the corner shop where Sally now worked.

Hilda's departure to keep house for her old employer Dr Lowther in Derbyshire paved the way for Kevin and Sally finally to move into their own home — Number 13 — as owners.

Kevin's days of regret and loneliness were over as he faced the future with a sense of belonging and everything to look forward to.

Andrea Clayton got pregnant by Terry Duckworth and became involved in a family feud between her parents and the Duckworths.

When Kevin's family moved out in early 1985 the Claytons moved into Number 11. Andrea Clayton, the family's intelligent young daughter, still at school and full of promise, took up with Terry Duckworth and horrified her parents by becoming pregnant. The running battle between them and their next-door neighbours, Jack and Vera Duckworth, did little to help the situation. The Claytons left Weatherfield before the baby was born.

Another unmarried mum was Maggie Dunlop, who'd been living with Mike Baldwin. She ran a successful florist's business and was in every way her own woman. Mike and Maggie got on really well and respected each other's abilities. Neither felt dependent on the other, but Maggie's pregnancy changed all that and she shattered Mike's dreams of a son and heir by leaving him to move out and, later, marry someone else.

Mike lost a son but hoped to set matters straight when he courted and eventually married Ken Barlow's daughter Susan. Sadly the marriage fell apart after Susan aborted Mike's baby. Ken must have felt some satisfaction over Mike's agony even though it left his daughter broken-hearted, confused and eager to leave Weatherfield for ever.

≤ SUSAN BARLOW'S DILEMMA ≥

'There's nothing you can say Dad. Nothing that can change the way I feel about Mike.'

Susan Barlow's wedding day on 14 May 1986 was the end of a troubled time in her young life. For a start, her father Ken was not going to attend the ceremony and she was to be given away by her twin brother, Peter. Then, her husband-to-be Mike Baldwin, many years her senior, was not at all bothered Ken's absence — he was quite happy to live the rest of his life without ever seeing him again.

When Susan came back to Weatherfield after having lived most of her life in Glasgow with her late mother Val Barlow's parents, she came back into a very tense atmosphere that existed between Ken and Mike. As she gradually fell in love with the eligible boss of Baldwin's Casuals who had a luxury flat, a Jaguar and a thriving business, she could not understand the tight-lipped animosity of her father.

Was it jealously? Ken was not well-off, he ran a small free-sheet newspaper and drove an old Volkswagen. There was certainly *something* Susan didn't know about. Something which had turned two neighbours who had occasionally had a drink together into enemies who would do anything to do the other down.

There was *something*, and, as the wedding day approached, Ken was forced to give Susan an explanation and make her think about the man she was to marry. The facts were as unpalatable to Ken as they were shocking and hurtful to Susan.

Mike had embarked on an affair with Ken's wife Deirdre in late 1982 and she had been on the very point of leaving Ken when she had seen the folly of her actions and decided to stay with Ken at Number 1.

Susan Barlow was caught up in the battle between her father Ken and her lover Mike Baldwin. She married Mike in 1986 but left Weatherfield after he disowned her for aborting their baby.

What Ken didn't tell Susan was that opportunist Mike had moved in on Deirdre when Ken was languishing in a boring council job, smarting under the loss of an expected promotion and paying less than a loving attention to his young wife. Mike's motives were totally selfish and he was quite prepared to break up a family to achieve his ends.

With all that in the past as Ken and Deirdre rebuilt their marriage and with Ken just establishing himself in his new vocation, the last thing he wanted or expected was suddenly to find his hated enemy standing on his doorstep.

The thought of Mike Baldwin becoming one of the family, sitting in on Christmas dinner and, eventually, fathering grandchildren of Ken's own blood was a thought so distasteful to him that he all but excommunicated himself from his daughter.

Deirdre, vulnerable and unsure as

to her role in the drama, was forced to look on while the past was publicly aired and even her daughter Tracy was dragged into the fraught atmosphere of the days that preceded the wedding.

While Mike made token shows of goodwill and 'forgive and forget', Ken was firm in his intention to have nothing to do with the alliance. It was in a troubled state of mind that Susan woke up on her wedding day. She loved and respected Ken, but she also loved Mike who, compared to Ken, appeared forgiving and only too happy to heal the breach.

At the eleventh hour, Ken stepped in to give her away — he even managed to assume an air of detatched congeniality, but neither Mike nor Deirdre were fooled. Ken had put his seal of approval on what he considered an abomination, for Susan's sake, but from here on there would be little contact between him and his son-in-law.

Susan's happiness was complete. She felt she was married to a kind, considerate man of substance and Ken had been won over. How could anything or anyone spoil her future now?

The times had certainly changed since 1902 when illegitimacy was a moral scandal worthy of suicide, and abortion, if discovered, would result in a long prison sentence!

A relationship that embraced sadness, disappointment and drama, and yet was always viewed by the onlookers with a little humour, was that between Derek Wilton and Mavis Riley. It was a long, up-and-down courtship, conducted over many years.

THE LONG COURTSHIP OF DEREK AND MAVIS

'Sometimes I feel that I'm in the back of a huge queue and all the women in front of me are getting good jobs, freedom of choice, equality and men. And it's never going to be my turn.'

The wedding of Derek Wilton and Mavis Riley in November 1988 was the culmination of a courtship that had lasted over ten years and seen Derek married and divorced, Mavis sharing a tent on a lonely mountainside with another man, and the pair of them skulking in darkened rooms believing themselves each to have ruined the other's life by failing to turn up for their wedding.

This was most out of character for Derek Wilton, ever fearful of his mother's shadow, and Mavis Riley, the shy, sensitive product of a teetotal and religious home.

Mavis had met Derek in the Kabin when he came to sell confectionery and later stationery. She was wont to blush at even the slightest familiarity with a man, but was attracted by his witty patter and obvious good intentions. A true romance looked set to blossom until Mrs Wilton, in whose dread poor Derek lived constantly, declared Mavis unsuitable after just one meeting.

Having spoken, Amy Wilton had to be obeyed and Mavis was ousted from Derek's social list. He put in an odd appearance now and then, to keep Mavis' hopes alive, but always left again abruptly and in unhappy circumstances.

Mavis was frequently let down by Derek, which left her blushing and often very angry and resentful, but somehow she couldn't bring herself to give Derek his marching orders. For his part, in spite of the hostility he received from Mavis' friends, who saw him as an irritating opportunist, Derek came back time and time again like a bad penny.

Eventually, in 1984, Derek managed his first proposal and the wedding was all arranged. Just before this, Mavis had gone away with a fellow night school student, Victor Pendlebury, on a walking holiday during which time they shared a tent. However, Mavis was quick to point out, when questioned about the circumstances, that they had used one tent but definitely *two* sleeping bags.

With all their past problems forgotten, Derek and Mavis prepared for the big day and the final break from independence. Each assured the other that they knew what they were doing and couldn't wait to get married. But, secretly, both had doubts and looked to the final break with the single life,

(Left) Mavis Riley, the shy and retiring spinster who eventually became Mrs Derek Wilton.

(Right) Dithering Derek Wilton, high in moral fibre but lacking in application.

The long-awaited and twice attempted marriage of Derek and Mavis finally took place on 9 November 1988.

which had held them for over forty years with some trepidation.

As the guests waited in the church, an argument flared outside as a result of matron of honour Rita Fairclough's arrival with the news for Derek's sister Edith, who was waiting for the best man, that Mavis had backed out at the last moment. Edith's acrimony was cut short when Derek's best man arrived to say that Derek, too, was not going to appear.

The thought of being married had proved too much for both of them. They were too set in their ways and neither was *sure* that marriage was what they really wanted.

Derek left the area once again and eventually married Angela Hawthorn, the daughter of the owner of Hawthorn's Stationery, in whom he possibly saw a chance to achieve commercial success. Mavis, meanwhile, carried on as before working for Rita at the Kabin still thinking of Derek and wondering why the affair had turned out so badly.

But true love will out, and he returned one night in a rain storm to propose, ignoring his married state, with a card that was thrust through the Kabin letterbox. He told Mavis his marriage had failed and he had now seen her in her true light as his one and only love. Once again, Mavis fell victim to the strange attraction that continued to bind them.

After Derek's stormy divorce, which saw them hiding from Angela's observers and Mavis being named quite wrongly as co-respondent, they both finally arrived at the church for their second wedding ceremony. Happily, the wedding went smoothly and Derek and Mavis Wilton began their life together after a honeymoon in Paris.

Victor Pendlebury, Mavis' old friend, still lurked in the background and Derek's propensity for misfortune still prevailed as fate preyed on the Wiltons, but still Derek and Mavis had each other. They were both agreed — the 12-year courtship had been all worthwhile.

Annie Walker finally retired from the Rovers Return in 1984 after 45 years as a lady publican. She left to live with her married daughter Joan in Derby.

The Rovers Return, which had been in the hands of Jack and Annie Walker since 1939, had always been a typical alehouse with a 'snug', a 'private' bar for the ladies and elderly regulars, and the main bar, which provided excellent ale from the hand pump, darts, and food in the form of sandwiches and rolls. A noisy and often drunken company passed many happy hours in the almost Spartan surroundings.

The widowed female publican, Annie Walker, retired in 1983 and went to live with her daughter in Derby and used emotional blackmail to force her son Billy to come and run the Rovers. His management was a disaster as he disregarded fixed opening hours and bought spirits from the cash-and-carry. The Walker empire ended when Billy sold out to the brewery. Brewery director, Sarah Ridley, appointed barmaid Bet Lynch as the first single manageress in 1985.

The fire caused by potman Jack Duckworth's less than expert

electrical repair work in 1986, ended the old Rovers' era. While Bet Lynch slept upstairs an inferno raged below, and only prompt action by Kevin Webster, who spotted flames behind the Rovers' glass door, and climbed in through the window, saved Bet's life. The blackened ruins that remained after the conflagration were scheduled for demolition, and Bet Lynch looked like losing her life's ambition.

However, the brewery reconsidered the demolition of their original flagship in the area and decided on an extensive rebuilding programme with upholstered drinking booths, bar snacks and keg beer. The most notable alteration, though, was the one-bar layout in which the Snug was dispensed with for ever.

Bet was an excellent barmaid with a friendly smile, a smart quip and a ready eye for a thirsty punter, but as a business woman, she was a total failure. Financially, the running of the Rovers got so bad that eventually she just took off and left the mess she'd created for someone else to sort out.

Alec Gilroy, who had a vested interest in the Rovers, having lent Bet a large part of her stake, was immediately hot on her heels to Torremolinos, where he found her working as a waitress, and he talked her into returning. Alec's money was at stake and he was prepared to consider anything — even a marriage proposal — to get her back to the fold. They returned, to marry and confound the cynics by being both successful and happy together. Alec had come a long way since he first saw the light of Weatherfield.

Billy Walker never fulfilled his mother's high hopes. He ran the Rovers briefly after her retirement, but it was a disaster and he eventually left in 1984.

⤜ ALEC GILROY — BORN TO ENTERTAIN ⤛

'I could 'ave been big. We're talkin' London Palladium, Vegas, Lord Grade. What did I get? The Alhambra, Weatherfield, Ramsbottom and Whistlin' Billy Cooper!'

Number 4 Back Gas Street is an address which does not have the ring of success about it. But, had things gone according to plan, and fortune smiled more kindly on one of its inhabitants, a pale blue plaque would have been attached at some future date. For here was born Alec Gilroy, now a publican, but at one time, set for a brilliant future in show business.

Alec and his sister Edna were both attracted to the smell of greasepaint at an early age. This was just as well as Number 4 was noted for its peculiar smell, which owed a lot to its proximity to the gasworks. Reg, the head of the household, was employed there as a stoker. The smell was augmented by the persistent odours that attached themselves to the clothes of Alec's mother, Mabel, who worked at Tasker's glue factory.

Edna was older than Alec and even at an early age was able to perform a song like a hardened trouper. She could sing *Any Old Iron* with a style

169

that would have delighted even Harry Champion, its greatest performer.

Alec was not lacking in theatrical ability and, trying to keep up with Edna, built up a passable turn that involved using trained ferrets. As a duo, they performed at weddings, masonic functions and football club dances until Edna got married and Alec's ferrets were mischieviously released into the night after a particularly noisy and drunken evening at the Weatherfield Rugby Club.

Alec had to seek other employment and, by quoting his vast theatrical experience and taking a position for a percentage of the take, he managed to acquire a job backstage at the Weatherfield Majestic just at the time that variety was on the wane.

All the top acts had gone to television and cabaret, so the Majestic was left with bird impersonators, slackwire acts and strong women who tore up telephone books. As Alec's percentage dwindled, his knowledge of speciality acts grew. Soon, he became noted for his ability to locate a farmyard impressionist and a balloon bender, agree payment terms, and have them performing out front all in the same day.

In 1955 he left the afternoon matinée of *Paree Pleasures* to marry Joyce Crosby, daughter of Harry Crosby ('Bing' to his intimates), who played a musical saw. Alec and Joyce had met backstage where she dressed and tended to her father's needs. Never slow at selling himself, Alec had acquitted himself well and, painting a picture of life at the top in show business, for which he was inevitably destined, he so impressed Joyce that she accepted his proposal.

Alec's first step on the ladder was promotion to front of house, where he presented a dashing figure in his tuxedo and white gloves. He continued to place his speciality acts but many now were becoming past it. Balloon bending and slackwire walking are not good companions to old age and one by one his old contacts fell away as gradually all the old patrons deserted the Majestic

In 1971, the neon Majestic sign came down to be replaced by the troupers' nightmare word 'Bingo', and Alec was without a job. He was also without a wife as Joyce and little Sandra, born in 1958, moved out to live with footballer Stan Shaw, known to the faithful followers of Weatherfield County as 'Clogger'. Clogger's reputation, and Alec's lack of appetite for the physical side of marriage, had meant there was to be no reconciliation after Joyce left and Alec busied himself in his agency work.

In 1975 he had the good fortune to meet theatrical agent Joe Blunstone, who at eighty was ready to retire. With 100 acts on offer Joe felt he had a good asset to dispose of and Alec, with hardly a penny in his pocket, but a persuasive manner, offered Joe 50 per cent of the take for the rest of his life. He made the offer after having carefully noted Joe's laboured breathing and frequent use of an inhaler. Joe agreed and duly received £50 for the first week. *The Stage* noted Joe's passing one week later and Alec attended his partner's funeral with a sad face and a cheque for the next instalment in his pocket which, somehow, never managed to reach Joe's grieving beneficiaries.

Heartache behind the smile: in 1971 Alec's wife Joyce left him, taking their daughter Sandra with her.

His first signing to augment the clientele of the late Joe was a red-headed singer called Rita Littlewood but, unfortunately, high as Alec's expectations were, the Blunstone Gilroy Organization, as Alec renamed it, started to dwindle.

The top acts, who'd joined Joe in their youth and stayed on only for his sake, left for better offers and, once again, Alec was left with mainly speciality acts who, talented though they were, were very small-time. Alec, was able to use some of the acts himself as he moved into clubland where he managed various local night spots. Eventually, he became manager of the Graffiti Club in Rosamund Street for the brewery, Newton and Ridley.

In time, he realized that he was to be no new Val Parnell or Lew Grade, and 'Alec Gilroy presents:' would never head the bill at a top venue. On the other hand there would always be a spot for the Mezzonis, Windy

September 1987: Bet Lynch and Alec Gilroy are married after Alec flew to Spain to bring her back. Many believed the marriage would not last.

Walleys, Miss Angel Cloughs, and Frank and Kitty Hebditches of this world. As long as they were able to perform, Alec would always be there to place them and make his percentage.

It was in 1987 that Alec turned his eye to the licensed trade and, with Bet Lynch, the unmarried manageress of the Rovers, in dire financial straits, he saw an opportunity to acquire both a wife and a new business. In spite of public opinion that his courtship of Bet was financially motivated, Alec and Bet married in September 1987 to become one of the stablest couples in the street, despite Bet's illustrious past and Alec's devious dealings.

From time to time Alec's theatrical past would come back to remind him, but, sadly, it was usually to attend a funeral of an old client or commiserate with a bereaved relative.

The sweet smell of success had somehow eluded Alec Gilroy, but as he rang up another large Scotch for a businessman or amassed a pile of pint pots to accommodate another round for a party of heavy drinkers, he drew great consolation from the knowledge that although speciality acts may come and go, ageing voices may falter and memory men may forget, the need to take a drink in good company will never wane.

Don Brennan and Ivy Tilsley married in 1988. Later, in the summer, they visited Blackpool sands with the young Tilsley family.

Down the street, at Number 5 Coronation Street, the Tilsley family, Bert, his wife Ivy and their son Brian, was hit by double tragedy when Bert died after a period of unemployment, disability and melancholia and then Brian was knifed to death in an alley outside a night club.

Ivy was shattered by the tragedy and often at odds with her daughter-in-law over her children's religion and her unwillingness to devote her life to the memory of Brian. Eventually, happiness returned to Ivy's life when she married mini-cab driver Don Brennan and honeymooned in Capri.

A few years before, an exotic holiday would have been well out of bounds for most Weatherfield honeymooners. The fortunate would have gone to Southport, the very fortunate to Torquay but, by now, Benidorm, Torremolinos and even Malta, where Ken and Deirdre Barlow enjoyed a holiday in 1983, were quite commonplace holiday destinations.

Hilda Ogden's 'muriel' and flying ducks were her pride and joy. She took the ducks with her when she went to work for Dr Lowther in Derbyshire in 1987.

The new Euro-awareness was also responsible for the departure of Elsie Tanner, whose flamboyant behaviour had for years fed the local gossips, when she left to join old flame Bill Gregory in his British-style bar in Portugal in 1984.

In 1987 Hilda Ogden suffered a terrible ordeal when she was the victim of a violent attack by burglars in the house of her employers, Dr and Mrs Lowther. Hilda was knocked unconscious and Mrs Lowther had a heart attack brought on by shock. After a spell in intensive care, Hilda emerged scared and insecure. She made her house at Number 13 a fortress with double locks on the doors and the windows securely fastened. Her ordeal only ended when she accepted Dr Lowther's offer to be his housekeeper and left her once-loved house for his expensive home in Derbyshire.

Her leaving party in the Rovers at Christmas 1987 was a rousing send-off by her neighbours, who saw, in the departure of the elderly gossiping charlady the end of yet another link with the past.

CHAPTER 12

1989-1992: BRINGING IN THE NEW

The bouncing Bettabuy logo which taunted the small shopkeepers, like Alf Roberts, with its pledge to save money by reduced prices.

APART FROM A short three-year break from 1968 to 1971 when maisonettes stood on the site, the side of Coronation Street opposite the old terrace had always housed a thriving business, from the early Victorian mill run by Mr Hardcastle to Elliston's factory, to the Mark Brittain warehouse and finally to Baldwin's Casuals. In 1989 the bulldozers moved in on the site and the building, along with the original Weatherfield Community Centre, was flattened. For all in Coronation Street and Arkwright Street it marked a drastic change.

Arkwright Street had been named in 1968 after the maisonettes had been built. It was a tiny lane running between the flats and the old warehouse that had once housed Hardcastle's goods. Maurice Jones, the property developer who had bought the land and demolished Baldwin's, tried in vain to buy the warehouse in order to build on the land. The Council refused his application, deeming the building to be of historical interest; instead they allowed him to demolish the community centre that was hardly ever used now a bigger centre, with extensive sports facilities, had been built on Inkerman Street. While Arkwright Street ceased to exist in the redevelopment scheme, Coronation Street boomed as the new houses and businesses built on the old site of Baldwin's brought modern architecture, gardens and a more open layout to the once cramped street.

For the first time in 90 years the residents breathed fresh air instead of stale smoke from the shadow of towering, oppressive factory buildings. The overpowering sound of works' hooters was replaced by the sweet, lyrical sound of birds singing.

Certainly one of the most distressing events of this rapidly improving era was the mental trauma suffered by Rita Fairclough, who ran the Kabin newsagents, at the hands of her lover, Alan Bradley. He was changed by circumstances from a well-balanced, successful business man into a violent, disturbed fiend.

≫ ALAN BRADLEY'S REIGN OF TERROR ≪

'People have treated me like dirt for long enough. The gloves are off now and I'm going to do all I have to to get what I want.'

Alan Bradley came to Weatherfield in 1986 when his estranged wife Pat was killed by a car and his daughter Jenny was left with only her grasping aunt and senile grandmother, already in a home, to care for her.

Jenny had been delivering newspapers for Rita Fairclough at the Kabin and as the bond between them grew, Rita decided to foster Jenny. Alan was a frequent visitor to the Fairclough household, and when he moved to Weatherfield to find a flat so he and Jenny could be together, his freindship with Rita soon turned into romance.

Alan was an attractive, seemingly level-headed man of the world with a definite eye for the ladies. Although he was paying court to Rita, and the two of them had a fine old time together, he also found time for Gloria Todd, the Rovers' barmaid who occupied a flat in the same premises as Alan and Jenny. Eventually, with his eye for the main chance, Alan burned his boats with Gloria and moved in with Rita to enjoy, to all outward appearances, a happy family life with her and Jenny.

A glimpse of Alan's past emerged when he knocked Terry Duckworth unconscious in the Rovers, after Terry had made a jibe about Gloria. He later confessed to Rita that he was possessed of a violent streak which had made him 'known to the police' on a previous occasion. The Duckworths did not proffer charges but Rita was well aware that Alan Bradley was a bit more than a cuddly pussy-cat.

With Rita's building yard as his modest headquarters for his security business, it wasn't long before Alan became a man of substance and turned his thoughts to marriage. He proposed to Rita and was turned down. Then, he set up a surprise wedding, confident that Rita would go through with it, only to have his plans dashed as Rita left in a huff.

Alan was devastated. Here he was, a personable, successful man, highly regarded by the ladies, and Rita had turned him down twice. He concluded there was no future for them and now turned his thoughts into making the best of the situation.

He had already borrowed £6,000 from Rita to set up his business, although he'd actually spent it on a showy new car, but now he needed more in order to move the business to new, more prestigious premises in Rosamund Street. By secretly assuming Len's identity from papers taken from Rita's documents, he managed to obtain £15,000 on the security of the deeds of Number 7 Coronation Street. He knew that Rita's property was in no danger since she was the genuine owner and she'd signed nothing.

Business prospered until Alan's roving eye and fiery temperament caused a scene with his attractive young showroom manageress, Dawn Prescott, who accused him of attempted rape and told Rita of his fraud in obtaining the loan.

Rita was at once devastated at Alan's advances to Dawn but angry and vengeful at his deception. She threatened exposure to the police and Alan snapped and almost killed her in his rage.

After a short spell on the run, while Rita's resentment built up and Jenny's concern for Alan was clouded by her realization that he was now branded a violent criminal, Alan was captured, put on trial, pleaded guilty and, although sentenced, was released immediately because he had already served six months on remand.

Jenny Bradley was befriended by Rita Fairclough when her mother died. She then introduced her father, Alan Bradley, to Rita and a romance developed.

Terry Duckworth, was the first to provoke Alan Bradley to reveal his violent streak.

Alan Bradley was a contented man until his business fraud was discovered, then the violent side to his nature surfaced — with a vengeance.

Alan Bradley left court with revenge in his heart. He considered himself cheated by Rita, who had not only robbed him of his freedom and his good life, but appeared to be robbing him of his daughter as well.

While Rita became more and more disturbed by Alan's menace, he obtained a job on Maurice Jones' building site in Coronation Street and used his proximity to torment Rita in their private exchanges while keeping up the public image of a penitent only out to make good for his sins.

Eventually, Rita cracked and disappeared without trace. Even Alan was astonished at this and he now became the focus of all attention as the possibility of Rita's murder was freely discussed and accusations made.

When Rita's whereabouts became known to Alec and Bet Gilroy after a tip-off from a hotelier in Blackpool, they found her living in the past, with her mind cast back fifteen years. She'd mentally shut-off all the recent horrors and was now working as a singer as she had all those years ago.

While Bet stayed to console her, Alec returned to tell Alan what he believed to be the good news that Rita had been found. Alan was far from delighted — he felt he'd suffered unjustly by Rita's actions and even been arrested on suspicion of murder. His main object now was to bring Rita back to Weatherfield, prove to everyone she was still alive, and get on with his life.

As he bustled her towards his car, after he'd accosted her in the street outside her seafront hotel, she made a dash across the road. Alan followed and was mown down by a tram — he died instantly.

While Rita wept and received Bet's consolation, Alan Bradley's body lay crumpled on the pavement but feet away.

Alan Bradley's reign of terror was over.

Newlyweds, Des and Steph Barnes, bought a house on the newly developed site in Coronation Street in early 1990 at a specially reduced price as Steph was Maurice Jones' daughter. Derek and Mavis Wilton moved into Number 4 after Derek had been promoted to Northwestern manager of Pendlebury Paper Products and needed a suitable home to fit his new position.

✦ ENTER DES AND STEPH ✦

'Peas in a pod, that's me and Steph. We could be twins. Wouldn't be so much fun though, if we were.'

The street's first yuppies, Des and Steph Barnes, moved into one of the new homes on the south side of Coronation Street on their wedding day, St Valentine's Day 1990. Their flaming row on the doorstep was typical of their stormy relationship that finally ended in separation after less than two years.

When bookie Des Barnes grinningly presented the smartly dressed young lady with a pint of lager, the last thing he expected was to receive it back in a most undignified manner. The Oval Bar at the Midland Hotel had seldom seen such a performance as that Saturday evening in December 1989 when Des and his two pals dropped in for a drink after a football match at Old Trafford.

They had already been drinking, first at half time and then in a pub outside the ground. So when they arrived at the plush surroundings of the Oval Bar their boisterous laughter and loud voices attracted some attention from its sedate, well-behaved clientele.

Des Barnes married Stephanie Jones on St Valentine's Day 1990. Their tempestuous marriage eventually ended only a year later.

As Des dumped himself down into the nearest chair he tilted it back only very slightly, but just enough to jar into the chair of the attractive young lady, sitting with her parents behind him, causing the cocktail she was about to raise to her lips to cascade down the front of her dress, cucumber slices, lemon, maraschino cherry and all. She took Des's apology quite calmly as she brushed herself off, accepted his compliment that he couldn't have bumped into a nicer lady, anywhere, and readily agreed to Des's offer of a replacement drink. Smugly, Des summoned the waitress to take the order and was slightly surprised when the girl ordered a pint of lager.

The waitress left to get the order and Des turned his chair round to introduce himself properly and further appraise his good fortune in coming across such a good-looking girl. Opposite, her parents, Maurice and Carol Jones, shuffled uneasily as they observed their daughter's slightly tense answers to Des's banal chat. They knew their Stephanie, too well, and the signs were not good.

The waitress returned with a single pint of lager, a bowl of nuts and a bill for £1.50. Nonchalantly, Des tossed down a fiver on the tray, told her to keep the change, elaborately laid down the bowl of nuts on the table in front of Stephanie and presented the glass to her with a deep bow.

Stephanie took the glass, stood up and slowly emptied the contents over Des's head. The grin faded as the nuts followed the drink to leave Des very wet and crowned unattractively with peanuts and cashews.

While Des spluttered, Stephanie stood back and her parents sank down behind their menus as she delivered to Des such a tirade of stinging abuse that even *he* blushed. When she was finished, she calmly gathered up her bits and pieces and led her mesmerised parents into the French Restaurant.

For some moments, Des sat and dripped, then, to hoots of laughter from his two companions, he stalked angrily towards the door of the restaurant where a bulky head waiter blocked his way.

As he caught sight of Steph, looking very beautiful in the soft light of the restaurant's ambiance, his anger faded. And when she acknowledged him with just the suggestion of a wink, he knew he would be returning to the Midland on the next Saturday and every following Saturday until their paths crossed again.

Meanwhile the workers from Baldwin's Casuals suffered from its closure as they lost their jobs and, although paid redundancy, they felt bitter at the loss of a secure income. Their ex-boss, Mike Baldwin, celebrated his new-found wealth and leisure by moving further south to the dock area where he paid £65,000 for a luxury two-bedroom flat. Once an area of high unemployment, crime and poverty, the disused quays had been built upon and now expensive apartments looked out across the River Irwell. However, it was not long before Mike lost his wealth when he invested in a Spanish property deal that went wrong.

The Bettabuy supermarket on Albert Road — the sixth store in a national chain started by Lord Morgan in 1969 — provided much needed employment for some of the women who had been laid off by Baldwin's. Run by manager Reg Holdsworth, the store had a reputation locally for being bad payers, and the assistants used to fight amongst themselves over who were to operate the check-outs where they were paid an extra £1 an hour. As well as coping with the mediocre wages, the assistants had to dodge Reg's unwelcome attentions and constantly wandering hands.

⇘ REG HOLDSWORTH'S WEAKNESS ⇙

'A Holdsworth is worth holding on to.'

Reg Holdsworth had been manager of Bettabuy in Weatherfield for just over a year in early 1990. He had been with the company for 17 years. When he became manager it was seen by him as a victory over his arch rival Brendan Scott who had dogged his steps since Reg had 'investigated' him on Bettabuy's behalf in 1981. Brendan had been suspended and moved

Reg Holdsworth (left, at age 18) came from Wig Street. A docker's son, he became the first in his street to enter a grammar school. He became general manager of Bettabuy in 1982.

sideways where he obtained a position in Head Office from which he was able to watch Reg's progress with a keen and critical eye.

Businesses had to be run efficiently and from the point of view of in-store efficiency and profitability, Reg and his able assistant-manager Norman Watts could not be faulted. However, Reg had an Achilles heel which could, at any time, lead him into a situation where the avenging Brendan Scott would strike.

Reg's weakness was women and no sooner was he ensconced in his office at Weatherfield, than his roving eye fell on female store detective Renée Dodds. Reg's romance with Renée was the talk of the store and came as quite a shock to his assistant manager, Curly Watts, who was at the time, pursuing his own lustful quarry in the shape of Kimberley Taylor. While Curly operated in the clean air of Weatherfield and maintained his gentlemanly courtship, Reg lusted and sweated behind the coffee bags in the store room where he was once caught with his clothes off with Renée by a shocked but mindful Curly.

Reg was to become well acquainted with that same store room when his wife, Veronica, eventually snapping under the strain of his infidelities, kicked him out of the marital home and caused him to take up secret residence at Bettabuy.

He established a permanent residence when Alf Roberts, a local shopkeeper, took pity on him and, even though a deadly rival in the provisions trade, offered him a haven in the flat above his shop. From here, Reg quickly set out to establish himself as a Casanova with the local ladies — married or unmarried, Reg was out to charm and win.

Reg was elegant and eloquent, but success with women for once eluded him, and when Alf finally expelled him from the flat for poaching his business, all he had to show for it was a clutch of 'adult reading' magazines, which Alf hurled from the window to be noted by all in the street below.

Next to catch Reg's attention was widow Rita Fairclough who, while not in any way seeing romance in their association, agreed to accompany him to ballroom dancing, but when Reg rigged a store competition in Rita's favour, his efforts won him the disapproval of Rita and investigation by Brendan Scott which did his promotion prospects no good at all.

Rita was prepared to forgive that little piece of double-dealing and still be friends, but the final straw came to break the back of their relationship when Veronica Holdsworth, from whom Reg was supposed to be divorced, arrived at the Kabin to accuse Rita of being his 'latest fancy piece', and gave her a run down of Reg's past affairs. Reg's attempts to explain away the misunderstanding fell on barren ground and he found Rita's door locked and barred to him.

Reg was not a person to stay down for long, his high self-esteem saw to that. In spite of constant rebuffs and positive statements by Rita that she wished to see no more of him, he persevered and bought the flat next to Rita's in the street. Eventually peace was made and Rita and Bet Gilroy joined him in a champagne celebration at his flat warming (he had invited just Rita). He confessed to being as happy as he'd ever been in the company of his new friends and neighbours, and assumed they felt the same way.

Reg Holdsworth was now a recognized member of Weatherfield society. With all the skeletons in his cupboard laid bare and Veronica Holdsworth far away in New Zealand, he was ready to launch himself into the social whirl of Coronation Street.

However, eyebrows were raised when the details of Reg's furniture and fittings were revealed by Bet and Rita. Unable totally to abandon his past proclivities, Reg had acquired an asset which most residents of the street would have regarded as pure decadence: his bedroom was now dominated by a quivering passion-pit of a water bed.

Curly Watts joined Bettabuy as assistant manager in 1990. He had enjoyed a varied career since moving into Coronation Street as Emily Bishop's lodger in 1983. First he was a dustman with unusually good educational qualifications, then he became a student in business studies. On obtaining his diploma he took the job working for Bettabuy.

≈! CURLY WATTS' LOVELIFE ≈

'What is this fatal attraction I have? Sometimes I'm petrified of my magnetic sexuality. Is no woman safe?'

Jack Duckworth, Curly Watts' former landlord, told him he'd finally cracked it when he left and moved into Number 7 Coronation Street with design student, Angie Freeman in early 1991.

Curly Watts with his favourite women: Angie Freeman (left) and Raquel Wolstenhulme (right).

At the time, he was Bettabuy's assistant manager and was known to be involved with the comely Miss Bettabuy from the cheese counter, Raquel Wolstenhulme.

From 1989, Curly had been lodging with Jack and Vera Duckworth and was engaged to another Bettabuy's assistant, Kimberley Taylor, whose parents' high moral code ensured that

the relationship stayed platonic. Kimberley was very moral, but had all but joined Curly on a stay at a country hotel when his plans were discovered by her parents, who promptly ordered their daughter to end the relationship.

Raquel Wolstenhulme, Miss Bettabuy 1991, had come along just at the right time and was able to offer herself willingly to have a good time with Curly. And so Curly arrived at Number 7 in the role of lodger, co-tenant or paying guest, but decidedly *not* lover to Angie.

His opportunities were obvious and womanisers such as Jack Duckworth, Des Barnes and Mike Baldwin remained unconvinced by Curly's assurances of their platonic set-up as Raquel was seen coming and going from Number 7 and Angie was seen exchanging pleasantries with Curly at the Rovers before both returned to their home.

Eventually, they came together when, low in spirits, each had a setback: Angie's fashion designs had been plagiarised and Curly had been given the heave-ho by Raquel who had left for London to become a photographic model. Over several bottles of wine, and with much self pity, Curly and Angie came together for one night of passion. Next day normality returned and they were back to their usual co-tenants status.

The allotments down by the canal were cut back by the Council who planned to build a new theatre on the site. The last theatre in Weatherfield had been the Alhambra on Clarence Street which changed to a bingo hall in the Sixties, and was later demolished in 1979.

Audrey Roberts decided to move out of Coronation Street for a better quality house and she and Alf set up home in a semi-detached property by the golf course in December 1989. Their house at Number 11 was bought by serving soldier, Jim McDonald, who was nearing the end of his military service and looking for a house to accommodate himself and the rest of his family, which included Liz, his brassy wife, and their sons Steve and Andy.

≥≥ LIZ AND HER DASHING SOLDIER ⩾⩾

'If I'd 'ave known I would be marryin' the whole flamin' British Army I may well 'ave not bothered saying "I do".'

Liz McDonald was glad to be moving into Number 11 Coronation Street in December 1989. For the last 15 years she and her husband Jim had lived in different army barracks around the world. Often Jim had gone abroad on his own and Liz had been left alone with the children. Now, she was to have a permanent home, and, thinking back, she remembered all her hopes and aspirations as a teenager... .

Liz Greenwood was in between the Bay City Rollers and David Bowie when she first set her sights on big Jim McDonald. It was a difficult decision to make but, for Liz, the most important of the day. Ronnie Richmond's record boutique in the city centre, where she and her school friend Sharon worked on Saturdays, had much to offer and the choice of one 45, which she was allowed each week as well as the three pounds Ronnie paid them, was normally the highlight at the end of the day.

Deep in thought as she thumbed through the latest releases, Liz was unaware that a customer was behind her drumming his fingers with impatience as he waited to be acknowledged. Eventually, when she was asked loudly whether she was serving or a customer Liz spun round ready with a quick retort but was stopped in her tracks when she was confronted with a soldier in the smartest uniform she'd ever seen.

Liz had a thing about uniforms and big Jim McDonald certainly wore his with style. He also had a sparkle in his eye and was amused by the effect he'd had on the pretty, but over made-up young Liz. Even when she countered his repartee, telling him she *was* serving but had to clear up after messy customers, he still held all the cards.

Liz Greenwood fell madly in love with Jim McDonald, but it was not in her teenage plans to be the mother of baby twins before she was 18.

He told Liz he was buying the records for a party at the barracks that night and, if she and her friend would like to come, they were welcome. Liz took down the address with a shaking hand but still tried to imply to Jim that she received invitations like this all the time.

It was only when he'd gone and Liz had dashed over to tell Sharon the good news that she realized she didn't even know his name. At the Greenwood's house in Henderson Street, as they made their preparations for the big night out, Mrs Greenwood preached caution, saying soldiers were just the same as sailors — a girl in every town — and they'd both better watch out.

The minicab arrived and the two girls set off in their flared jeans as wide as their feet, bare midriffs and platform shoes that made them look about six feet tall. Questions were asked when they arrived at the barracks gate especially as they didn't know the name of their host for the evening. But when Liz described him as 'six foot six with a stripe on his arm and a funny accent', the guard sent them on telling them to ask for Jim McDonald.

It was a noisy, fun-filled night as the soldiers let their hair down away from the day's disciplines and the girls, quite a few of whom Liz recognized from school, made the best of the plentiful food and drink.

Liz was disappointed that Jim was so much in demand and not able to spend much time with her. But Sharon had found herself a sober-looking Scotsman and sat down happily in a corner, deep in conversation. Liz was at a loose end until Jim finally shook off all his other admirers to spend the last half hour with her. She had had plenty of offers to dance earlier but didn't want to put Jim off.

In spite of his outward bluster, Jim turned out to be quite a serious-minded person and Liz found herself trying to think up some erudite

Sergeant Jim McDonald was a member of the Royal Engineers. He turned down a job at the recruiting office and finally left the army at the request of his wife, Liz.

conversation with which to hold his interest. Jim was just happy to be in her company and, apart from the odd fiery outburst when someone else asked Liz to dance, was at peace with the world and keen to tell her of his family in Ireland.

Suddenly, the party was over and Jim was insisting he take both Liz and Sharon back to Weatherfield in a cab. To the end, he was the perfect gentleman and after a sedate goodnight kiss made a date for early next week — a date that led to many more.

Despite Nancy Greenwood's warning, Liz fell head over heels for her soldier, who had only a few weeks left in England before taking up a posting in Germany. At school, in her last term, Liz was the object of much envy as she showed off the little jewellery gifts and items of clothing bought for her by her well-off boyfriend.

The first sedate kiss in the taxi developed into a lot more over those last weeks and when Liz found to her horror that she was pregnant, Jim didn't even bat an eyelid — he proposed marriage there and then.

Nancy Greenwood was not *told* what had happened but wisely she did not oppose Liz's wedding plans so vehemently as her husband George, who suspected Liz had taken leave of her senses. Jim and Liz were married at St Thomas' Church on 5 January 1974 with Sharon as maid of honour and Jim's best pal Johnny Johnson as best man.

Next day, they left for Jim's posting and married quarters in Germany. In three short months, Liz had progressed from the sixth form at Weatherfield Comprehensive and Ronnie's Record Boutique, to a foreign posting in Germany and a family due at any moment.

Young Liz McDonald had a lot to look forward to in those early days of 1974 but would never in her wildest dreams have imagined herself as a wife and a mother of twins before she was 18 years old.

Steve and Andy McDonald, the twin sons of the McDonald family of Number 11 Coronation Street, proved to be as rebellious as any

Andy (below left) and Steve McDonald. Whilst Andy stayed on at school to study A levels in Maths, English and Computer Studies, Steve left and signed on the dole.

Victoria Arden was forced to leave her comfortable Cheshire home after the death of her parents in 1991. She moved to the Rovers to live with grandfather Alec Gilroy. He allowed her to keep on her horse Saracen, despite the cost.

A reporter from Radio Weatherfield interviews Bet and Alec Gilroy locked behind closed doors, during the Yankees saga.

of their teenage contemporaries. Andy even contemplated leaving home when his scholastic achievements appeared to go unlauded by his parents. They seemed to favour his less academically gifted brother Steve, who himself reacted angrily to his parents' ban on his association with 15-year-old Joanna Khan, by taking off with her to the Lake District, sleeping rough and generally causing his parents and Joanna's such a deal of trouble that they were at each others throats. But the romance foundered as they experienced the pressures of being penniless and homeless. They argued and went their separate ways.

Joanna was almost sexually assaulted before she arrived home and Steve was sweating over the washing-up in a run down hotel before being rescued by his mother and brought back to Coronation Street.

Industrial estates continued to thrive in the area, built on waste land or bomb sites, they housed factories and offices close to main roads leading to motorways. Peter Ingram's textile firm operated from the Sharp Lane industrial estate. After his death from a heart attack in 1990, his widow Jackie married Mike Baldwin. Everyone in Weatherfield felt sorry for her as they were convinced that he was marrying her for her money.

In June 1990 the Rovers Return was threatened by an innovation that would have made Aubrey Newton, who had performed the opening ceremony in 1902, turn in his grave. The brewery, in the shape of its henchman Nigel Ridley, decided to turn the traditional, long-established pub into 'Yankees', a brassy American bar with Confederate flags, 'wanted' notices and a pianist.

Alec Gilroy was totally in favour of the venture as he saw himself making an increased income, but the locals, championed by his wife Bet, fought to keep it the same and the Rovers stayed with tradition, even though at one stage, a prospective new publican was sent to take over.

Following on with tradition, 90 years after Commercial Lane was renamed Rosamund Street in honour of music hall singer Rosa Hanbury, local girl Sally Webster went into labour on Christmas Eve 1990. She was rushed to hospital in a minicab but the baby was born on the way. As her daughter was born in Rosamund Street, Sally named her 'Rosie', not realizing the historical connection.

Ken and Deirdre Barlow became a casualty of modern times when Deirdre, pushed into Council politics by Ken, took her job too seriously. Ken felt she was neglecting him and daughter Tracy and he started an affair with another woman, Wendy Crozier. Ken moved away for a while but returned to take up the flat over Alf's mini market. The couple's divorce was finalized in February 1992.

In over 90 years, Coronation Street had changed. The abject poverty of Edwardian England had given way to an era where even people like the Duckworth family could be assured of enjoying a good living, a two-week summer holiday abroad and a car of their own.

The very symbol of 1992 must be the Bettabuy supermarket in Albert Road where the shelves carry an immense variety of consumables which would have been held in awe by the street's original residents. The price of one shopping basket today, added up in a few moments on the electronic till, and paid for with a credit card, would have kept the entire Coronation Street of 1902 well fed for one week.

Meanwhile, in the summer of 1992 Alma Sedgewick, who ran the café in Rosamund Street, was well aware of change — she had a difficult decision to make about her future happiness. She knew her ultimate decision would affect the rest of her life dramatically.

The Webster family of Number 13 Coronation Street. Their daughter Rosie was born in a cab in Rosamund Street on Christmas Eve 1990.

◁ ALMA MAKES A DECISION ▷

'The only sin I've committed is knowing Mike Baldwin. And I'll be regretting that for the rest of my life.'

As the morning traffic weaved its way into the city, up Rosamund Street, Alma Sedgewick faced her future. The 48-year-old café owner had suffered a great deal of emotional turmoil over the past three years. She had to be

Alma Sedgewick knew that Mike Baldwin deceived her, but she just couldn't resist his charm and compelling personality.

The ill-fated wedding of Mike and Jackie Ingram in mid 1991 was over within weeks.

Ken and Deirdre Barlow in 1989, with their daughter, Tracy. The marriage was doomed when Ken embarked on an affair with Wendy Crozier.

certain that the step she was about to take would be the correct one — should she marry Mike Baldwin?

It was early morning in June 1992 and at midday she was due at the registry office. The event was planned in detail, the honeymoon was booked and the guests had bought their confetti in anticipation of the big event. Alma had longed for this moment ever since she'd first seen Mike. Now it was here she wasn't sure it was what she really wanted.

True, she found Mike irresistible, his charm, wit and basic sex appeal left her breathless, but she was all too aware of the other side to his nature. Mike Baldwin was a manipulator, always ready to use people to achieve his own aims. He had two broken marriages behind him and countless broken hearts and lives. She knew that he was as hard as nails and thought only of himself, but one look at his boyish smile and she couldn't resist.

The chemistry she shared with Mike was unlike anything she had ever known before. Her ex-husband Jim Sedgewick had never thrilled her in the same way. He had been solid, reliable and *boring*. Theirs had basically been a marriage of convenience when she had thought she was pregnant. It had been a false alarm and ironically, a year later when she *had* got pregnant they had both agreed an abortion was the only answer as there was little enough love in their relationship to share with a child and both were regretting being so tied down already.

They had gone their separate ways in 1982, six years after their wedding. Jim had taken up with a florist and she had gone to live in America with Philip, a well-built Pools winner. But Alma soon discovered that well-oiled biceps soon lost their appeal without a brain to deal with the sharks that were after his money. She watched as Philip was led into a web of sex, drugs, booze and bad investments that left him penniless and friendless. At the end of the affair, Alma was left with little more than her fare home.

All Alma had salvaged from her marriage had been the café and the flat above at 12 Rosamund Street. Mike had entered her life but had soon dropped her for a 23-year-old blonde. She should have learnt by her mistake but when he apologized, smile, and dangled the keys to his luxury flat in front of her, she relented. The year 1990 had been beautiful, full of expensive meals, romantic weekends away and long mornings spent in bed. Little did she know that Mike was going off to spend his afternoons in someone else's bed.

Factory owner Jackie Ingram had enticed Mike away from her and had married him, but that hadn't lasted a month. As soon as Jackie threw him out Mike had been back on Alma's doorstep, apologizing for his behaviour, sending flowers and wearing down her strong resistance. She had fought her feelings towards him and had even managed to have an affair with teacher Ken Barlow.

But all that had changed. Mike had frightened Ken off and she had allowed him back into her life. After turning down his first marriage proposal, to teach him a lesson, she had accepted his second. To her friends' amazement, Alma had let Mike make the engagement announcement in the Rovers Return. Why were they amazed? They all knew how much she loved Mike, how much she had longed for him. The whole of Weatherfield knew Alma Sedgewick wore her heart on her sleeve.

Mike had hurt her, not once, not twice but a hundred times. Could he ever be trusted not to hurt her again? Would he stop lying, scheming, manipulating? Would there be more blondes or wealthy factory owners? Had he gone too far or did he really care?

With a sigh in front of the mirror, Alma made up her mind.

Martin Platt with his two step-children, Sarah Louise and Nicky, and holding his own son, David, who was born on Christmas Day 1990.

Martin Platt from Number 8 Coronation Street was seen as a most unconventional person. Eyebrows were raised when he first courted, then moved in with twice-married Gail Tilsley (who was ten years his senior) and her two children. The predicted break up — when Martin tired of the older woman — never came and the romance blossomed into marriage.

Once again cocking a snook at the image of the macho male, Martin willingly became a 'house husband', cooking, shopping and looking after Gail's two children and his own son, David, born some time before the wedding.

He made a good job of his duties until a move into the most expensive house in Coronation Street (purchased for £38,000) necessitated a return to work where still Martin defied convention by training to be a nurse.

The last survivors of the early days of the street disappeared with the departure of Ena Sharples and the death of Albert Tatlock in the early 1980s. Now, only the cobblestones and the houses on the south side of Coronation Street remain as a relic of the historic day in 1902 when the street was first born.

As old and new combine and the past lies buried beyond memory, the twenty-first century looms and, with it, almost certainly a Coronation Street as rich in human joy and suffering as the one already known.

Terry and Lisa Duckworth's wedding poses were interrupted when Terry, released from prison under guard for the ceremony, took off in the middle of the photo session and made a dash for freedom.

WHO'S WHO

The cast list includes the years the characters were resident in Coronation Street, and their occupation.

JANEY ATKINSON
Barmaid, 1903

GLADYS ARKWRIGHT
Caretaker, 1902-1937

MIKE BALDWIN
Factory owner, 1976-1977

DAVID BARLOW
Footballer/shopkeeper, 1942-1968

DEIRDRE HUNT/LANGTON/ BARLOW
Typist/shop assistant, 1977-

FRANK BARLOW
Postman, 1938-1964

IDA LEATHERS/BARLOW
Kitchen hand, 1938-1960

IRMA OGDEN/BARLOW
Shop assistant, 1964-1971

KEN BARLOW
Teacher/editor, 1939-

SUSAN BARLOW/BALDWIN
Fashion buyer, 1965-1987

VALERIE TATLOCK/BARLOW
Hair stylist, 1961-1971

DES BARNES
Bookie, 1990-

STEPH BARNES
Sales assistant, 1990-1991

EMILY NUGENT/BISHOP
Shop assistant/clerk, 1967-

ERNEST BISHOP
Photographer/clerk, 1972-1978

JERRY BOOTH
Plumber, 1963-1975

ALAN BRADLEY
Engineer, 1987-1989

JENNY BRADLEY
Student, 1986-1991

DON BRENNAN
Cabbie, 1988-

IVY NELSON/TILSEY/BRENNAN
Machinist, 1979-

SARAH BRIDGES
Barmaid, 1914-1915

FLORENCE HARDCASTLE/ BRIGGS
Landowner

AVIS GRUNDY/BUCK
Mill worker, 1921-1925

ALICE BUCK
Spinner, 1911-1915

JOE BUCK
Fusilier, 1911-1918

LARRY BUCK
Loom operator, 1911-1925

NED BUCK
Loom operator, 1911-1925

SARAH BUCK
Weaver, 1911-1919

ARMISTEAD CALDWELL
Resident of Jubilee Terrace

MINNIE CARLTON/CALDWELL
Weaver, 1962-1976

BILLY CHAD
Rigger, 1920-1938

FLO HEWITT/CHAD
Weaver, 1902-1938

GRANNY CHAD
Char lady, 1934-1936

IVAN CHEVESKI
Engineer, 1961

LINDA TANNER/CHEVESKI
Machinist, 1940-1961

ANDREA CLAYTON
School girl, 1985

HARRY CLAYTON
Milkman, 1985

LES CLEGG
Shopkeeper, 1968

GORDON CLEGG
Accountant, 1968-1969

MAGGIE PRESTON/CLEGG
Shopkeeper, 1968-1974

CHARLIE CORBISHLEY
Potman, 1902-1916

JIM CORBISHLEY
Landlord, 1902-1919

NELLIE CORBISHLEY
Landlady, 1902-1919

ALBERT CRAPPER
Miner, 1902-1906

JACK CRAPPER
Miner, 1902-1906

PEARL CRAPPER
Housekeeper, 1902-1919

RONNIE CRAPPER
Pawnbroker, 1902-1910

GEORGE DIGGINS
Landlord, 1919-1938

MARY DIGGINS
Landlady, 1919-1938

JACK DUCKWORTH
Fitter/potman, 1983-

TERRY DUCKWORTH
Entrepreneur 1983-1987

VERA BURTON/DUCKWORTH
Machinist 1983-

LEN FAIRCLOUGH
Builder, 1968-1983

RITA LITTLEWOOD/FAIRCLOUGH
Shopkeeper, 1977-

AUDREY FLEMING
Typist, 1968-1970

DICKIE FLEMING
Electrician, 1968-1970

LIL MAKEPIECE/FOYLE
Shopkeeper, 1902-1927

TOMMY FOYLE
Shopkeeper, 1914-1945

ANGIE FREEMAN
Student, 1990-

FRED GEE
Potman, 1976-1984

AMY GIBSON
Sales assistant, 1950-1960

TED GIBSON
Bookie's runner, 1950-1960

ALEC GILROY
Landlord, 1987-

BET LYNCH/GILROY
Landlady, 1970-

DOT TODD/GREENHALGH
Shop assistant, 1926-1945

AGGIE GRIMSHAW
Seamstress, 1902-1907

DANIEL GRIMSHAW
Miner, 1902-1906

PERCY GRIMSHAW
Miner, 1902-1904

CHARLES HARDCASTLE
Mill owner

MABEL GRIMSHAW/ HARDCASTLE
Landowner

MATTHEW HARDCASTLE
Mill owner

CHRISTINE HARDMAN
Machinist, 1939-1962

GEORGE HARDMAN
Clerk/shop keeper, 1930-1950

MAY HARDMAN
Housewife, 1930-1960

ENID HARRISON
Retired, 1902

LIZZIE HARRISON
Retired, 1902

ADA HAYES
Teacher, 1910-1949

ALICE HAYES
Housewife, 1908-1952

ESTHER HAYES
Clerk, 1924-1962

SIDNEY HAYES
Clerk, 1908-1940

CONCEPTA RILEY/HEWITT
Barmaid, 1959-1964

DOLLY HEWITT
Weaver, 1902-1905

GERTIE PEGG/HEWITT
Weaver, 1905-1926

HARRY HEWITT
Bus conductor, 1921-1964

LIZZIE HARDING/HEWITT
Machinist, 1948-1959

LUCILLE HEWITT
Shop assistant, 1949-1974

MARY MAKEPIECE/HEWITT
Spinner machinist, 1902-1936

SAMUEL HEWITT
Weaver, 1902-1909

THOMAS HEWITT
Weaver, 1902-1947

REG HOLDSWORTH
Supermarket manager, 1991-

TRICIA HOPKINS
Shop assistant, 1974-1976

ALAN HOWARD
Mechanic, 1970-1973

ELSIE GRIMSHAW/TANNER/ HOWARD
Sales assistant, 1939-1984

BLANCHE HUNT
Resident of Victoria Street

RAY LANGTON
Plumber, 1968-1978

ELSIE FOYLE/LAPPIN
Shopkeeper, 1930-1960

JACK LEEMING
Sorter, 1902-1904

MAGGIE LEEMING
Minder, 1902-1904

FLORRIE LINDLEY
Shopkeeper, 1960-1965

NELLIE LINGARD
Weaver, 1919-1929

TOM LINGARD,
Gardener, 1919-1929

VERA SHARPLES/LOMAX
Shop assistant, 1937-1946

MARTHA HARTLEY/LONGHURST
Resident of Mawdsley Street

PERCY LONGHURST
Shunter, resident of Mawdsley Street

MOLLY HEWITT/LONSWAITE
Barmaid, 1910-1930

DINKY LOW
Fusilier, 1917-1918

MADGE LOW
Weaver, 1917-1918

LIZ GREENWOOD/MCDONALD
Barmaid, 1989-

JIM MCDONALD
Engineer, 1989-

ALFRED MAKEPIECE
Weaver, 1902-1908

IVY MAKEPIECE
Washer woman, 1902-1938

RALPH MAKEPIECE
Docker, 1902-1916

SUSIE MAKEPIECE
Weaver, 1906-1925

WILL MAKEPIECE
Potman, 1904-1926

ALFIE MARSH
Mill foreman, 1913-1915

MO MARSH
Char lady, 1913-1916

HILDA CRABTREE/OGDEN
Cleaner, 1964-1987

STAN OGDEN
Driver/window cleaner, 1964-1984

MARY TATLOCK/OSBOURNE
Spinner, 1908-1918

THOMAS OSBOURNE
Tailor, 1908-1911

BEATTIE TATLOCK/PEARSON
Shop assistant, 1933-1953

EMMA PIGGOTT
Weaver, 1902-1918

FRED PIGGOTT
Foreman, 1902-1918

GAIL POTTER/TILSLEY/PLATT
Café owner, 1975-

MARTIN PLATT
Nurse, 1992-

CLARA POPPLEWELL
Spinner, 1902-1918

EMILY POPPLEWELL
Nurse 1902-1918

ERNEST POPPLEWELL
Slag puller, 1902-1903

HARRY POPPLEWELL
Storeman, 1902-1918

JACKIE RIGBY
Storeman, 1946-1950

ALF ROBERTS
Shopkeeper, 1978-1990

AUDREY POTTER/ROBERTS
Housewife, 1985-1990

RENÉE BRADSHAW/ROBERTS
Shopkeeper, 1976-1980

ENA SCHOFIELD/SHARPLES
Caretaker, 1937-1980

ALFRED SHARPLES
Resident of Inkerman Street

PERCY SUGDEN
Baker/caretaker, 1983-

THOMAS SWINDLEY
Local draper

LEONARD SWINDLEY
Haberdasher and lay preacher

ARNOLD TANNER
Sailor, 1939-1945

DENNIS TANNER
Salesman, 1942-1968

STEVE TANNER
US Army officer

ALBERT TATLOCK
Weaver and clerk, 1919-1984

BESSIE TATLOCK
Weaver, 1919-1959

CEDRIC THWAITE
Shopkeeper, 1902-1914

LOTTIE HOFNER/THWAITE
Shopkeeper, 1912-1914

BERT TILSLEY
Fitter, 1979-1984

BRIAN TILSLEY
Mechanic, 1979-1985

JACK TODD
Shunter, 1926-1946

JIM TODD
Desert Rat, 1926-1941

SALLY TODD
Shop assistant, 1926-1945

VI MAKEPIECE/TODD
Weaver, 1902-1944

BETTY PRESTON/TURPIN
Barmaid, 1969

CYRIL TURPIN
Policeman, 1969

ANNIE BEAUMONT/WALKER
Landlady, 1938-1984

BILLY WALKER
Mechanic/landlord, 1938-1984

JACK WALKER
Landlord, 1938-1970

CURLY WATTS
Binman/manager, 1983-

BILL WEBSTER
Builder, 1984-1985

KEVIN WEBSTER
Mechanic, 1984-

SALLY SEDDON/WEBSTER
Shop assistant, 1986-

DEREK WILTON
Salesman, 1990-

MAVIS RILEY/WILTON
Shop assistant, 1990-

RAQUEL WOLSTENHULME
Barmaid, 1992-

EDDIE YEATS
Binman, 1980-1983

ACKNOWLEDGEMENTS

The authors would like to express their gratitude to the following for their help in providing photographs for this book:

Miss Jean Alexander — Hilda Crabtree Ogden: p. 92
Mr Ivan Beavis — Harry Hewitt: pp. 85, 103
Mr Tony Broughton (estate of Arthur Leslie) — Jack Walker: p. 70
The estate of Margot Bryant — Minnie Carlton Caldwell: p. 58
Miss Beverley Callard — Liz Greenwood McDonald: p. 183
The estate of Violet Carson — Ena Schofield Sharples: p. 57, 61, 77
Mr Nicholas Cochrane — Andy McDonald: p. 185
Miss Elizabeth Dawn — Vera Burton Duckworth: p. 157
Miss Gabrielle Daye — Beattie Tatlock Pearson: p. 109
Miss Betty Driver — Betty Preston Turpin: p. 88
Miss Noel Dyson — Ida Leathers Barlow: p. 50
Mr Kenneth Farrington — Billy Walker: p. 101
Mrs Janet Featherstone (estate of Lynne Carol) — Martha Longhurst: p. 74, 75
Miss Joan Francis — Dot Todd Greenhalgh: p. 95
Mr Simon Gregson — Steve McDonald: p. 185
Miss Ruth Holden — Vera Sharples Lomax: p. 108
Mrs Betty Howarth (estate of Jack Howarth) — Albert Tatlock: pp. 31, 72
Miss Maggie Jones — Blanche Linfield Hunt: p. 114
Miss Anne Kirkbride — Deirdre Hunt Langton Barlow: p. 113, 142
Mr Charles Lawson — Jim McDonald: p. 184
Mr Stephen Lowe (estate of Arthur Lowe) — Leonard Swindley: p. 115
Mr Ken Morley — Reg Holdsworth: p. 179
Mr Bryan Mosley — Alf Roberts: p. 105
Mrs Janet Nagy (estate of Bill Nagy) — Gregg Flint: p. 94
Mrs Margaret Nelson (estate of Avis Bunnage) — Alice Hewitt Burgess: p. 84, 104
Miss Sue Nicholls — Audrey Potter Roberts: p. 151
Miss Daphne Oxenford — Esther Hayes: pp. 62, 127
Mrs Sheila Pemberton (estate of Frank Pemberton) — Frank Barlow: p. 80
The estate of Patricia Phoenix — Elsie Grimshaw Tanner: pp. 85, 98
Mr Alan Rothwell — David Barlow: pp. 86, 108
Mr Gerald Sim — Ted Farrell: p. 89
Miss Doris Speed — Annie Beaumont Walker: p. 67
Mrs Doreen Vines (estate of Maudie Edwards) — Elsie Castleway Foyle Lappin: pp. 82, 97
Mr Bill Waddington — Percy Sugden: pp. 99, 100
Miss Sally Whittaker — Sally Seddon Webster: p. 163
Mrs Teddy Youens (estate of Bernard Youens) — Stan Ogden: p. 91